THE CITY OF HOPE

The
City of Hope

SAMUEL H. GOLTER

G. P. Putnam's Sons
New York

Dedication

In the four decades since its founding, countless individuals and groups have participated in the building of the City of Hope, and their names are indelibly recorded in its annals. It would be impossible for me to give merited credit to each and every one of them in this book and consequently I shall refrain from making specific mention of places, projects, or people directly associated with its development.

Instead, I humbly dedicate this book to all those men and women, living and dead, whose dedication to an ideal first brought a unique institution into being upon the American scene—and then, they called it the City of Hope.

Acknowledgment

I WISH to express my appreciation and gratitude to Rose L. Watts for her assistance in preparing this manuscript. Her work exemplified the true spirit of dedication that is characteristic of all the people of the City of Hope.

Contents

Contents

*Illustrations will be found
following pages 52 and 116.*

Foreword

A SMALL TUBERCULOSIS SANATORIUM which came
into being on the West Coast because of conditions
on the East Coast at the turn of the century is the
background for my story. But this book is not concerned with brick and mortar. The physical development of the institution is only incidental to the series
of circumstances which led to its being called a "City
of Hope." There is a story behind that story. It
pertains to another series of circumstances which
seasoned my reactions toward the humanitarian principles adopted and practiced by the pioneers of the
sanatorium.

As it happened, I was one of the great numbers
of immigrants who came to the United States early
in the century. Among the many observations which
left an imprint on my inquisitive mind at that time
were the demoralizing effects of a disease—tuberculosis—which threatened to become epidemic among
the people who worked long hours in airless sweat-
shops and then went home to sunless tenements.

At that time, the disease was known as "consumption" because it relentlessly consumed the body—a ruthless and indiscriminate killer of men, women, and children. Deservedly it was called the "White Plague."

Consumption was infectious, there was no known cure, and general hospitals refused admittance to its victims. Stricken members of devoted families were often forced, or even chose, to leave their homes in the hope of preventing the spread of infection to those who had as yet escaped the scourge. The outcasts were herded into derelict and dilapidated buildings which had been thrown open for them along the crowded Eastern Seaboard. Each morning, those who had died during the night were carted out in full view of the survivors who were awaiting the same fate.

To escape these dread scenes, victims in all stages of the disease fled the industrial centers of the East. Fresh air and sunshine were thought to have curative properties, so consumptives—some with their families—flocked to the more sparsely settled areas in the West. Los Angeles became one of the meccas for them.

The first arrivals settled as best they could and then provided tents in their back yards or in empty lots for friends and relatives stricken by the disease, who followed them to California some time later.

It was during this era that an incident occurred

which spurred a handful of humanitarians to pitch two tents in the Duarte Desert, about twenty miles east of Los Angeles. A young man in the last stages of consumption, wandering homeless in a section of the city where the residents were predominately of Jewish extraction, suffered a hemorrhage, fell to the pavement, and died. The compassionate people of the neighborhood took up a collection to pay the cost of sending his body back East for burial.

Later, the same people called a mass meeting to discuss the need for providing a refuge for the needy victims of tuberculosis who came to Los Angeles in search of a cure. They collected one hundred thirty-six dollars and five cents and used the money to make a down payment on a few acres of desert wasteland. It was in 1913 that the two tents were set up—one for patients, the other for a nurse. Nothing could be done medically to save the lives of the patients but they were saved the indignity of dying on the streets. Such were the humble and humanitarian beginnings of the City of Hope.

As people continued to stream west from every part of the United States, the little desert haven began to assume a national character and, as it grew, sought national support. By word of mouth residents in all sections of the country learned about the struggling sanatorium in sunny California and regional groups began to organize themselves into auxiliaries.

In order to maintain support on an urgently needed recurrent basis, charters were issued to groups that engaged in fund-raising activities exclusively for the benefit of the sanatorium.

Emulating the principle of their adopted homeland which precludes taxation without representation, the immigrant founders of the institution gave the auxiliaries administrative and policy-making powers. Every second year, delegates elected by those groups convened in Los Angeles, to exercise their administrative prerogatives. To this day, the biennial Convention functions as the supreme governing body of the institution.

The broad humanitarian principles embodied in the first constitution of the newly created sanatorium were drafted by people who themselves lived in adversity. In the main, this book tells the story of the part I played in formulating their original concepts into a way of life. Since I firmly believe they constitute a constructive and fundamental pattern for the world of tomorrow, I have addressed this story to my seventeen-year-old daughter, Irma. It is with design, therefore, that I present and discuss certain phases of life which might seem to relate only indirectly to the history of the City of Hope itself.

SAMUEL H. GOLTER

THE CITY OF HOPE

1

Dear Irma . . .

IN SUBSTANCE, this story has been in the making for over a half-century now, and represents many pages torn from the calendar of my hectic and exciting life. But the idea of recording some of my experiences and observations for you dates back to an incident which occurred in the California Lutheran Hospital in Los Angeles within a few hours after your birth, on Christmas Day 1937.

You were in such a big hurry to arrive on this planet of ours that it was necessary to shield you from the harsh realities of life for a little while in the cloister of an incubator. As it happened, I was admitted to the hospital nursery for a close peek at you —and a wondrous bit of black-haired humanity you were. Just then a young couple entered for a visit with their baby. I saw them glance in our direction a couple of times and then, because of some acoustical quirk of the tiled room, I heard the young man whisper, "That must be a Jew baby."

A Jew baby! Just a few hours old, innocent of any offense, but you had already been tagged with an epithet which I knew from my own experience might cause you many heartaches through the years.

Then and there, I decided that if I could some day hand on to you my own ideas of why human beings sometimes find it difficult to act as humans, it might help to dull the sharp edges of your own experience. I would teach you to be tolerant; to understand that persecution, and other evidences of man's inhumanity to man, are remnants of the animal instinct which he has not yet managed to cast off on his long march away from the beast.

That was seventeen years ago. During that interval my concern for your welfare shifted away from the immediate scene and onto a broader plane, because man is snarling more than ever like a beast again. He has gone on a rampage, committing cruelties so unprecedented in human history that new words have had to be coined for their designation. The most frightening of them all is "genocide," defined as "the extermination of racial groups."

We have already fought several major wars in this half-century in an attempt to save the human values our ancestors accumulated so painstakingly during many centuries—all the religious, philosophical, moral,

4

and ethical codes which distinguish man from the lower animal. And now, leading the remaining free peoples of the world, our nation is once again engaged in a struggle with forces whose avowed objective is to destroy the glorious values for which we stand.

In my opinion, the ingredients contributing to the greatness of the United States are unique in history. I sincerely believe that if they are preserved, enhanced, and properly employed by succeeding generations, the United States will continue to be an influence for good in the world for a longer period of time than other nations and empires which reached great heights in the past and then declined.

I am convinced that each of us, individually, can consciously influence our world for good or evil. If that premise is correct, your attitude toward, and relationship with, your fellow man might well have a vital bearing on the future greatness of the United States, and even on the future course of the world.

You and your contemporaries must never forget that liberty and justice for the individual and all the other democratic principles which have been incorporated into our national life are the fruits of a seven-hundred-year struggle by Western man. You must have the vision and the courage to protect that priceless heritage. It was the respect for individual rights and dignity that led our nation to encourage spirited people, who were denied those privileges in their respective homelands, to come to these shores. Here they were permitted to practice their individual cultures and customs which, in turn, strengthened and enriched their adopted country. They were allowed freedom of speech, of religion, of travel, of action. In short, our nation has encouraged cultural pluralism to an extent unequaled by any other heterogeneous people that ever flourished on this earth, and that is the most potent device yet developed for maintaining the balance and counter-balance necessary for a strong and free democracy.

You must always remember, however, that man's progress is evolutionary. Some of us have not yet reached the stage at which we can adjust, wholly, to a composite of religious and racial cultures and the acceptance of one ethnic group by another cannot be forced by enacting laws to that effect. But it is not vital to the strength and virility of our nation that we all "love" one another, using the term literally. Until the ideal status of universal brotherhood has been reached, it is important only that we "respect" one another as Americans, whether our ancestors arrived on the *Mayflower* or in some more recent immigrant tub.

The competitive spirit has been an accelerating force in the unprecedented progress of our nation and I believe that every American who contributes to its development has a right to share in its power and glory as a first-class citizen.

It is my conviction that every individual has an inalienable right to be selective in his choice of associates. Acceptance or nonacceptance on the social level is not a consideration in the longevity of our nation or the welfare of its people. But you must strive to keep our courts of law, educational facilities, and industrial channels free from discrimination for reasons of race, religion, color, or creed.

I believe, further, that man's most prized asset is his dignity and that hope for the continuation of our way of life in these United States—perhaps our very survival as a great nation—lies in the preservation of and respect for the dignity and worth of the individual. To attain that noble objective, it is necessary for each individual to strive for an inner conviction of his own equality with others. Similarly, each ethnic group must strengthen its own consciousness of equality, asking and giving recognition on a basis of accomplishment, if our nation is to continue to derive strength from its plural heritage.

Now you are seventeen. The interval since my first resolve to record these thoughts for you poses another and more personal consideration. Though we all find the reality difficult to accept, man is mortal. His years on this earth are measured by just so many revolutions around the sun. My count is already high and I may not be available for counseling you later, when your need is greatest. That is why I am anxious to evaluate some of the occurrences of the past half-century for you, now, as they relate to the planning of the new society you and your generation are destined to build.

And here I want to insert a word of caution. You of the younger generation, who take over the management of our world, must not hesitate to break with the past and embrace the trends of the future. The worship of tradition is detrimental to progress when it is carried to extremes. In this dynamic era which marks the birth of a new cycle in our civilization, yesterday's guideposts are not always reliable precedents for tomorrow's action.

This story, then, treats that period of my life during which I was given the opportunity to build an experimental laboratory in human values, known as the City of Hope. I shall touch only briefly on those experiences and observations of the years before which influenced my attitudes toward the work which became the compelling interest of my life.

For my purpose, therefore, the story begins in 1926. . . .

2

Pioneers

WHEN I ARRIVED on the scene, the little tuberculosis sanatorium in Duarte, California, was thirteen years old. The first accommodations, two portable tents set up on a sweep of desert in the foothills of the Sierra Madre Mountains, had already given way to a small community of ten or eleven nondescript frame cottages and a few stucco units. The buildings had been added one by one over the years, without allegiance to a master plan, and they were scattered about haphazardly over the sandy, rock-littered terrain.

I had been in Los Angeles for just a few months of a planned twelve-month sojourn when a former acquaintance who, coincidentally, was the executive director of the institution, asked my help in reorganizing its physical facilities. Stipulating a three-month time limit, I agreed to his proposal.

Specifically, it was on June 5, 1926, that I took

up residence at the sanatorium which was then popularly known as the JCRA. The full corporate name, however, was "The Jewish Consumptive Relief Association of Southern California."

I immediately set to work familiarizing myself with the service program, getting acquainted with the personnel, and appraising the available facilities. Most of the buildings were poorly constructed, there were no hard-surfaced roads, no walks, no landscaping. All in all, its physical appearance could be described only as "bleak." And yet, from my very first day at the JCRA, I was aware of an unaccountable "something" in the air that reduced those material faults to relative insignificance. Before too long I had identified the mysterious element as a spirit of kindness and good will which was manifested toward the patients to a degree that was unprecedented in my experience.

That was a time when an early diagnosis of tuberculosis was rare and, as a result, a cure was even rarer. Everything then known to medical science was being done to effect the physical recovery of the patients, but medical interference was still totally ineffective in halting the relentless progress of the disease, once it had taken firm hold on its victim. So it was out of an immense pity for their helplessness against the disease that the founders and supporters of the sanatorium were determined to preserve the dignity of the suffering people who, through force of circumstance, became recipients of free care.

Observing this humanitarian principle was almost a religion among the early pioneers of the institution. Most of them were poor in material resources themselves, but they were always ready to make personal sacrifices, if necessary, to support that merciful and idealistic practice which was, and is, so unique to charitable works.

Curiosity eventually impelled me to learn more about the people who had inspired that attitude and I began to spend a part of each day visiting with the eighty patients housed in the sanatorium at that time. Many of them were little more than adolescents, the children of tuberculous parents who had known little or nothing about the need for taking protective measures against the highly infectious disease. Our patients came from all sections of the nation and represented many nationalities and religions—a truly heterogeneous patient population that did, however, have at least two things in common. They were engaged in war against the same cruel and relentless enemy, and their chances of survival were meager.

The broad policy of nonsectarianism practiced by an institution almost entirely supported by Jewish people was another element of its operation that came as a revelation to me. I had heard many preachments on the subject of man's brotherhood, but never

11

before had I seen it practiced so religiously. The only prerequisite for admission to the sanatorium was the need for its services.

I happened on still another singular feature of the sanatorium's operation when I was reviewing its organizational setup. The founders, most of whom were immigrants, had patterned its administration on the democratic processes of their adopted country. Every person who contributed to the support of the institution, if only to the extent of one dollar a year, was entitled to a voice in the election of its leadership. Yes, representation for one dollar a year!

So many elements in the makeup of that desert haven seemed to me to emanate from the human spirit that I was completely captivated before the three months I had allocated for my services were up. I was already favorably inclined to forego my former pursuits and stay on at the sanatorium, when its Board of Directors offered me a newly created position with the imposing title of "Superintendent."

It was then forty-four years after Robert Koch, a German country doctor, had announced to the world that "consumption" was caused by a live organism resembling a tubercle. He called it the Tubercle Bacillus, or TB for short. In that long interval, little progress had been made toward the development of an effective medical weapon against the disease, and the doctor's presence at a bedside had little more than psychological significance. If he happened to be a sympathetic human being, the doctor could serve a far more vital purpose than the few ineffectual prescriptions he so solemnly wrote down. Unfortunately, among institutional doctors especially, there was too often a lack of interest in the patient as an individual. In large measure, this attitude was an outgrowth of a humdrum routine which offered little challenge to a man who had devoted many years to the study of the art of healing. But rationalization could not ease the heartbreak of watching the pitifully weak flame of hope in the eyes of a mere youngster flicker and go out, when a doctor considered it his professional duty to be brutally frank about the hopelessness of his condition.

As time went on, my interest in the patients began to take precedence over the administrative problems. Little by little I shifted some of the detail of my office to an assistant, usually an ex-patient, so I would have more time to spend with them.

The turnover in our family of patients was gradual but unremitting. A few of them left the hospital of their own accord but the large majority left under cover of night, on the way to the great unknown. The waiting list was long, replacements almost immediate, and there was a continuing need for the suggestion of optimism in an atmosphere otherwise charged with despair.

In this life-and-death drama, I gradually began to assume the role of father, brother, and counsellor. Each morning, after my desk was cleared of administrative detail, I started on my rounds, going from bed to bed speaking words of hope and encouragement, in an effort to sustain morale. I also served as the sounding board for the individual grievances of the patients. For the most part they had to do with the perfunctory performance of the doctors, from whom the patients expected more than was in their power to give.

For the patients, curfew was nine o'clock. For me, the dimming lights signaled a return to my quarters but not for sleep. Driven by a growing sense of personal responsibility for the welfare of the patients, I spent most of my evenings poring over the many medical books I had added to my small personal library. To compensate for the lack of specific training in the field which I knew was to become my life's work, I read endlessly on the subject of tuberculosis, the evolution of medical science, and the history of the medical profession, relating my findings to the pertinent problems that arose during the day.

My work was all-absorbing and spiritually rewarding. As I read and studied, I often paused to reflect on my good fortune in happening on a vocation that satisfied the desire I had known from childhood on —to be of service to my fellow man.

14

3

Good Samaritans

IN LOOKING BACK over the devious routes I had traveled toward my destination, I discovered a true paradox. For at least twenty of my then thirty-six years, I had been preoccupied with the fight against "man's *inhumanity* to man." And yet every crossroad, every turning, brought me closer to that minute spot in the Duarte Desert where I found myself among people whose credo was man's *humanity* to man.

Led by my sightless soul, I had traveled halfway around the world to my destiny.

As a youth in Czarist Russia, I had seen ample evidence of man's inhumanity to man. Human life was cheap in Eastern European countries even then, and personal dignity was considered the sole prerogative of the ruling classes. While giving lip service to the principles of Western civilization, they suppressed and persecuted their subjects without mercy. I grew

15

up resenting the oppression of the people and my indignation finally gave me the courage to break family ties when I was sixteen years old. In 1906, I emigrated to the United States because I had been told that all people enjoyed equal opportunity there. Then followed the excitement and anguish of adjusting to my new homeland. I was determined to become a contributing factor in the early industrial development of a nation which encouraged rather than feared individual initiative.

In 1920, I spent many harrowing months in Eastern Europe as a member of a Relief Mission, helping to "bind the wounds" of the innocent victims of that holocaust which was a death blow for human values —the First World War.

In 1926, the stresses and strains of two decades of hectic activity, capped by the appalling evidence I had seen in Europe of man's return to bestiality, took their toll of me physically, mentally, and spiritually. On an impulse, I boarded a ship, sailed out of New York Harbor and, via the Panama Canal, headed for sunny California to rest, to think, and to reorient my perspectives on human life and human behavior. And then I happened on a desert oasis, where I was to find nourishment for my starved spirit.

I could not help but wonder about the nature of the Good Samaritans there who had given me free rein to maintain an atmosphere of kindness and good will for helpless victims of life. It did not seem logical to me that coincidence alone would account for the fact that so many of the philanthropic TB sanatoria were under Jewish auspices. Why, then, of all immigrant groups who streamed to the United States at the turn of the century, did only the Jews establish free sanatoria for tuberculous outcasts?

In musing on this phenomenon, I came to realize that the dedication of the people of the sanatorium to the principle of saving human life had far greater significance than met the eye. Actually, it was part of a pattern of conduct which had its origin in the fundamental laws created by a Semitic tribe called the Hebrews, as they wandered homeless in another desert, many centuries before.

Thinking back to my childhood, I could almost hear again the monotonous intonation of my stern religious tutor, as he drummed ironbound injunctions and prohibitions into my head, often with the application of a rod: "Do not boil the kid in the milk of its mother"—the humanitarian basis for *kashruth;* "Do not kindle fire on the Sabbath"—literally, "Set aside one day each week for rest"; followed by more of the same. "Do not—do not—do not!" Then, when he felt that I had absorbed the significance of all those laws which committed me to a way of life, he would remind me, with equal emphasis: "But remember! You may violate all these laws for the sake of saving human life!"

Permission to breach those fundamental laws, which were held in such reverence by the Jews that they were guarded and preserved intact during long centuries of persecution and adversity, attested, as no other example could, to the infinite value placed on human life by that Semitic tribe called the Hebrews.

The contrast was so great between the inhumanity prevalent in the world and the humanitarian principles fostered by the founders of the sanatorium that I sought further for an insight into their motivations. I found the answer in a series of historic events which, in my opinion, disproved the widely held view that the Jews are a "Chosen People."

Currents and crosscurrents of history made them what they were, not divine intervention. They were an old people; they had held stubbornly to the idea of the dignity of man; they had been dispersed and persecuted for having the courage of their convictions; through the centuries they were denied nationhood in the geographical sense.

These factors contributed to their broad humanitarianism and their universal concepts. The same adverse circumstances conditioned them for the creation of a literature which fundamentally affected the course of civilization: the Ten Commandments, the poetry and lamentations of the Prophets, the Sermon on the Mount, the Epistles of Paul, the rich plots in the books of Ruth, Esther, and on, and on, and on.

The moral and ethical codes embodied in these writings were created and accepted by some of the authors as a pattern for a better way of life. Others attributed their wonder and beauty to divine origin and divine inspiration. Saul of Tarsus was in the latter category and succeeded in influencing a goodly part of mankind toward his point of view.

I was satisfied that I had found in these concepts the answer to the riddle of the Good Samaritans of the sanatorium and to their almost religious dedication to the saving of human life and the preservation of individual dignity. It occurred to me then that the practice of those values would be an effective antidote to the inhuman manifestations it had been my lot to observe along the road to my new little world.

4

Obsession

THE WAR between a cruel, merciless killer equipped with deadly weapons, and the helpless people who were forced to fight a relentless disease almost without weapons, haunted me day and night.

The youth of the patients also kept alive the bitter memory of a comparatively recent tragedy in my own family. I was a confirmed bachelor with no immediate family of my own and had unofficially adopted a favorite niece as my ward. When Dora was fourteen years old, her father died of tuberculosis. Alerted to the possibility that she might have contracted the disease from him, I took her from one doctor to another. They all assured me that she was all right but her frailty continued to disturb my peace of mind. At that time, altitude and rest were thought to be the most effective treatment for tuberculosis, so in the face of the doctors' assurances, I arranged for her to leave school and spend some time in a mountain resort.

About a year later, when I was preparing to leave for Europe again, I brought her home and provided for her partial support during my absence. When I returned to the United States two years later I found to my dismay that Dora was on her deathbed. She died during the latter part of 1925, just a few months before I left for the West Coast.

Her death, coupled with the many tragic evidences of tuberculosis I had so recently seen in Europe, convinced me that "consumption" killed more men, women, and children, prematurely, than did war. The TB problem became an obsession with me.

When I became affiliated with the sanatorium, I was a comparative newcomer to California and had not had time to make many friends outside the institution. As a result, I had little social life and was able to concentrate all my thoughts and efforts on the daily routine at the sanatorium which presented four distinct challenges.

First and foremost was the need to save and prolong the lives of the patients; second, to maintain their morale and preserve their dignity; third, to resolve the ever-present administrative problems of the institution; fourth, to spend as much time as I could spare with visitors to the grounds, in an attempt to arouse their interest and support of the sanatorium.

Nearby Pasadena was a winter resort and vacationers often visited the sanatorium. In addition to generous contributions, many of them carried word back to their home cities about the unique qualities of the small institution, and some of our most active supporters today stem from those early contacts.

The funds I obtained through those sources financed the establishment of our own dairy farm, a chicken ranch, additional buildings for patients, and many other welcome service facilities.

Even though I was not directly concerned with the fiscal problems of the sanatorium, and they were many, the help I obtained in this way often meant the difference between downright bankruptcy and merely keeping our heads above water. The JCRA was endowed only with idealism and devotion to the cause and was in financial hot water most of the time. Our income was always precarious—a collective total of pennies, nickels, and dimes—so of necessity it became our policy to "build first and worry afterward."

The first few auxiliaries attracted only those women who were genuinely interested in helping the helpless—true altruists. By and large, they came from families in the lower income brackets. People of means in the area did not participate, were openly opposed to the existence of the sanatorium, and tried their best to undermine it. They were afraid the institution would attract sick and undesirable people to the area who might ultimately become their involuntary financial responsibility. It seemed that those who "had" were more conservative than those who "had not." Monied interests in the region did not approve of the unorthodox financial practices of the group of "fanatical idealists" who, in their zeal to answer the pitiful cries for their services, expanded facilities without immediate economic wherewithal. At first, those policies seemed fraught with danger to me too, but I came to realize that the very hazards of our existence were a stimulating influence to the devoted and dedicated people who formed the lifeline of the institution.

"If the cause is right," those humanitarians insisted, "the money will come from somewhere." And somehow, it always did.

Members of labor and fraternal groups were the largest beneficiaries of our services, but at that time they were a meager factor in the support of the sanatorium. Labor was still engaged in its own struggle to determine whether our country's industrial might would be built by free enterprise and slave labor, or by free enterprise and free labor.

The time had not yet come when labor could take care of its members beyond the economic field, but in recognition of the broad humanitarian principles

23

upon which free services were provided for the
needy, without the soul-searing brand of charity,
labor groups did contribute to the sanatorium to the
extent of their meager ability. Their participation in
the early development of the institution, and their
continuing interest through the years, are evidenced
by the goodly number of our buildings and facilities
which bear the names of labor organizations.

The problem of obtaining day-to-day support was
not my immediate concern, however. I was interested
only in matters pertaining to the sanatorium itself,
as they related to administrative problems, to the
welfare of the patients, and to the preservation and
acceleration of the human values practiced there.

5

Chicago

THE DAYS at the sanatorium passed quickly but the nights were long. I had ample time then to muse over the day's activities, relating them to those events in the years gone by which had conditioned me for my life's work.

A meeting with a committee of labor representatives who visited the sanatorium recalled my immigrant days in Chicago, Illinois, and the part I had played in the early struggle there between capital and labor. That was a critical era in American history and marked the beginning of a new cycle in man's economic progress. Coincidentally, in terms of its ultimate effect on my own development, that was also the most significant period of my life.

It was then the practice in Chicago, when immigrant trains arrived, to load the newcomers into horse-drawn wagons and deliver them to their relatives and friends. Sixteen years old and agile, I climbed up on the high seat with the driver as the family groups piled into the back. The wagoner, who was a comparative newcomer to the United States himself, grew nostalgic about the Old Country and, since I was a voluble source of news, he saw to it that I was the last one to reach my destination.

Those who have never lived in a country where freedom is circumscribed can hardly appreciate my reactions to the New World. I was bursting with happiness and enthusiasm over this amazing land where people could ride almost halfway across the nation, and jog around a big city all day long without fear, and without being stopped even once by the police and asked for identification cards. Before I was deposited at the home of a family who had been former neighbors in Russia I had promised myself to acquire the language, the customs, and the loyalties of my new homeland by the shortest possible route.

The problem of obtaining employment and establishing economic security was not quite as simple as I had been led to believe. When I first arrived in the United States my worldly assets totaled four silver dollars, but they had been reduced to three en route to Chicago. At a stopover, I had gotten off the train to stretch my long legs and had tendered one of my precious dollars to a young vendor for a bottle of pop. He ran off to get change and that was the last

I ever saw of him. Yes, my very first business transaction in the New World was a fiasco! I knew it was wrong and I was hurt, but the incident with the dishonest pop seller did not dampen my buoyant spirits for very long. The twenty-five percent reduction in my capital did, however, emphasize the urgency of seeking employment.

My first job in Chicago was with a picture-frame factory, where I was "gainfully" employed at one dollar a day for twelve hours of work. To me, that was sheer luxury, because I was living in a free country—a young, pulsating, industrial nation that needed youth, enthusiasm, hard work, and a concentration on definite objectives.

It came as a shock to me, therefore, to discover that certain interests, engaged in a struggle, were using the same terrorist methods I had seen in Russia. I was on my way to work one beautiful summer morning when I saw an unruly horde of marching derelicts—tattered, unkempt, unshaved. They were hurried along by guards, made brave by the pistols bulging from their pockets. Was this Russia all over again? No, the element of abject terror was missing. When I learned that these ruffians, gathered from all parts of the nation, were being paid by employers to break a strike at one of the large stockyards, I was crushed. I could have told them, even at my young age, that when people are exploited, and denied recourse to justice, they revolt; that oppression begets oppression. I could also have warned them that the greater the intimidation, the more violent the retaliation. Proof of this was the widespread mayhem of the Nihilist movement in Russia, near the close of the nineteenth century.

It is a sad commentary upon human behavior that all progressive movements which aim to supplant an old order and usher in a new one must be paid for with human life, bloodshed, and misery. That sad reality has many precedents—the Magna Charta, the Protestant Reformation, the French and American revolutions, to name just a few. I wondered, on that summer morning, if the conflict for economic betterment in the United States was to follow the same nihilistic pattern, or whether a new, young, and enterprising nation would find another and more constructive way of solving this problem.

That was in the days when our nation was in the process of rapid industrial development. Management was acquisitive, ruthless, devoid of social consciousness, and workers were exploited unmercifully. There were then practically no labor laws. Children as young as eight years old worked in factories where they were bullied by brutal and sadistic foremen. I had actually seen youngsters taken by the neck and thrown out of the factory bodily for some trifling infraction of the rules, or for a minor oversight in their workmanship.

The City of Chicago, like the growing industrial centers farther east, attracted large bodies of immigrant workers. But unlike those in other cities, workers in the Midwest were restive and more eager to fight for collective security. Their aggressiveness could be traced, I believed, to the presence of large numbers of immediate descendants of those German refugees who had fled their homeland during the rebellions of the middle nineteenth century. They were a militant lot and took a leading role in the early progressive movements in this country. Their fighting spirit was manifested in the famous Haymarket Riot and other similar disturbances which they fostered and led.

When this resolute group subsequently joined forces with various brands of aggressive native unionists such as the Knights of Labor and the I.W.W., and then later drew added strength from the influx of a new and spirited vintage of Eastern European immigrant workers, the foundation was laid for the American labor movement as we know it today. Fortunately, their revolutionary mood was moderated by the cooler heads of their northern neighbors who were predominantly of Scandinavian stock. It is my impression that the evolutionary course they preferred to pursue in that industrial strife was the forerunner of the New Deal which, at its very inception, stole the thunder of the Socialist program in the United States. I felt even then that if we persevered in our efforts to further that economic philosophy, we could some day show the rest of the world the way to bread and freedom for all.

For a long time, labor remained the underdog in the pitched battle with capital. In order to turn the tide, it became evident that the naive, idealistic, and conscientious trade union leaders would have to give way to a rough and rugged leadership which could cope with the entrenched power on more equal terms. It was not long before those more aggressive pilots began to borrow and use the same ruthless tactics employed against them by industry, and to devise a few original ones of their own.

When avaricious and feudalistic capital finally did come to grips with the exploited workers, drastic measures had to be taken to establish a working relationship between the two factions. It was evident that industry, which, up to that time, had all the advantage and the law in its favor, would have to relinquish some of its power and replace the harsh and brutal taskmasters with more humane administrators.

By then, I had become a superintendent in one of the largest clothing manufacturing concerns in the United States. Paradoxically enough in that era of tyrannizing foremen, it was the fact that I understood the workers' problems and was in sympathy with their yearning for better working conditions that contributed to my rapid promotion. One of the owners of the concern was progressive—a rare specimen in those days—and he recognized that his more than four thousand employees would exert greater effort under kindly supervision than under duress.

As it happened, he had been a member of the Board of Regents of a large university in the outskirts of Chicago, and had come under the influence of some of its more liberal and progressive faculty members. Those young professors, many of Scandinavian descent, believed that it was in the best interest of our country for immigrant workers to be absorbed into its industrial development through a process of integration rather than exploitation. Industry wisely drafted the services of those farsighted young educators and they proceeded to lay a sound foundation for a collective bargaining system. Though I was not yet twenty years of age my employer asked me to serve as an advisor to the professors on matters pertaining to practical industrial problems. I remember how pleased they were to discover that I could also serve as a sounding board for the immigrant workers from whose ranks I had come.

It was my impression that many of the patterns for industrial relationships which ultimately were adopted by the rest of the nation were developed in Chicago at that time with the help of those clear-thinking young men. Their calm, cool Scandinavian temperament was a stabilizing influence in that tense struggle in which so many hot-tempered elements participated.

I spent a lot of time with those young, educated Americans and my admiration for them stimulated my appetite for knowledge and culture. Up to that time, I had had only Judaic religious instruction and they encouraged my search for secular knowledge, taking an almost paternal interest in my scholastic progress.

At that period in its history, Chicago was a cultural hub of the United States, offering unlimited opportunities to an educationally and culturally starved immigrant. During the day I worked, on week nights I went to school, and on Sundays I attended lectures. It was not easy. I had attained no great facility in the English language, and yet I was embarked on a course of study at college level.

During that golden era of culture in Chicago, educators and speakers of national and international repute presented their views in lectures and debates. I would spend all day Sunday running from one lecture hall to another, listening to such speakers as Horace Bridges—Ethical Culture; M. M. Mangazarian—Rationalism in Religion; Professor Foster, Dean of Theology in the University of Chicago—Progressive Christianity; Arthur Moore Lewis—Science, Economics, Socialism; Professor Percy Ward—Philosophy; Emma Goldman—Anarchism; Clarence Darrow, who would debate with anyone on any subject, taking either side. Topping that off, there was a Forum on the Near North Side, known as the Dill Pickle Club, where intellectual eccentrics had complete freedom to air their isms and credos.

The freedom of expression in those days gave me the opportunity to weigh the viewpoints held and propounded by all kinds of people, and taught me to beware in later life of zealots who insist that only their beliefs and way of life are in the best interest of the majority. I discovered that there are at least two sides to every question and that unless a person is entirely familiar with both sides, he cannot reach a logical and satisfactory conclusion. Exposure to all those divergent preachments also convinced me that a little antipathy toward blind conformity was pretty good insurance against entanglements that might lead to disillusionment.

My own respect and appreciation for knowledge led me to encourage my fellow immigrants to follow in my footsteps and seek an education. As the superintendent of a large plant, I had the opportunity to arrange working schedules to accommodate those who expressed a desire to attend school. I think it is safe to admit, now, that I often allowed the students to work overtime, even when there was no great need for it, so they could attend classes the next morning. From time to time, I run across men and women who credit their education to my encouragement and there are few things in which I take more pride.

It was during this period, too, that I became a proud citizen of the United States—a nation which I realized even then was destined to take the lead in fashioning a better world.

6

"When Sorrow Walked with Me"

WHILE THE administrative and supervisory duties were an important part of my daily routine at the Duarte sanatorium, I would not allow them to super-sede my interest and concern over the welfare of the patients. I was particularly impressed with the way nature helped these hopelessly sick people to make a mental and emotional adjustment when threatened with extinction. In many cases, the adjustment was so perfect that they were able to assume an almost nor-mal outlook on life, for a time at least, and I took ad-vantage of that phenomenon. I learned that the song of hope can be played on many strings and that under certain circumstances, even false notes ring true. I became convinced that false hope was better than none, and though I suffered severe pangs of conscience, I spread false hope on my daily rounds. Making plans for a nonexistent future helped to rouse the patients from the lethargy of despair and usually gave them a little stronger hold on life. But hope alone was not enough to stay the hand of death.

It seemed to me that a part of myself died with every patient who lost the fight. In self-defense, therefore, I wanted to keep my relationships with them on an impersonal basis. I had no favorites. They were all my friends.

Then, one day, in making my rounds, I noticed a newcomer in the section of the sanatorium known as the Women's Hospital. Young and pretty, she greeted me with a sweet, friendly smile as I entered the enclosed, corridor-like porch she shared with two other patients. Her name was Gertrude.

Before long, it became obvious to myself and everyone else that I was visiting the Women's Hospital more often than was necessary in the line of duty. Snatches of conversations with Gertie, as she became known to everyone, revealed that she had been born in the Ukraine and that every member of her immediate family had been put to death during the upheaval following the Bolshevik Revolution. With the help of certain agencies, she had managed to make her way to the home of an aunt in New England. As a result of long privation, however, she became an

36

easy prey to tuberculosis. Homeless and alone once again, she had come to the sanatorium.

She reminded me of my niece Dora, whose death from the same disease had caused me so much anguish, and it was against my better judgment that I eventually adopted Gertie as my ward. I had always made it a practice to bring back little inexpensive gifts for the patients when I went into Los Angeles and now that I had Gertie to buy for too, my shopping tours took on added interest and significance. Returning from one of those trips, I casually handed her a package and turned away quickly, hoping to give the impression that I was being entirely impartial and on a routine mission. But I did not fool anyone but myself.

On subsequent visiting days, Gertie's delicate beauty was enhanced by a pink bed jacket, and nurses, doctors, patients, and visitors, began to stop by for a word with the frail little bed-patient who was all dressed up for company. She delighted in those social visits and for a little while anyway she was a queen.

But her happy smile would suddenly give way to the wracking cough she could not control and we all knew that her heightened color, which gave an impression of rosy-cheeked health, was in truth the hectic flush characteristic of advanced tuberculosis.

For a long time I deliberately avoided consulting

the doctors about the true state of Gertie's health because I feared their prognosis. But when the hectic
flushes began to appear more often on her visibly
sunken cheeks, I summoned up the courage to ask.
With a tact and sympathy that were rare qualities,
the doctor intimated that Gertie was a very sick girl.
Then, hesitatingly, he added, "It won't be long."

I had heard that same verdict many times before
and it had always overwhelmed me with frustration
and discouragement. This time I was literally overcome by deep depression.

Early one afternoon about three weeks after my
conversation with the doctor, a nurse hurried up to
me as I was leaving my office. She did not have to deliver her message—I read it in her eyes. I ran down
the long corridor to Gertie's room and as I entered
the door she reached up her arms. Our first and only
embrace was in silent, desperate farewell.

I spent the rest of the afternoon locked in my room,
searching through my books for a philosophy, a
poem, a religious tenet, anything that might soften
the hurt of Gertie's death. Tragic enough in itself,
her death also magnified my guilt feelings over the
false hope I peddled, the false promises that plagued
my nights as I waited for the hushed wheels of the
passing hearse. There was hardly a night that one of
the patients—someone who believed in me and my

empty words of hope—was not carried away into oblivion. And now it was Gertie, who had fought her way to freedom, only to die.

Toward evening, I went for a lonely walk. In the distance, Mount Baldy looked down on the neighboring Duarte Desert, coldly unmindful of my frantic grief. On the opposite horizon, the setting sun silhouetted the mighty telescope perched on Mount Wilson. I knew that little earthlings were up there busily scanning the limitless universe through the powerful lenses, hoping to find a clue to its elusive mysteries. In fancy, I wondered if a new star would not appear in the galaxy that night—a star marking Gertie's celestial paradise.

Night falls fast over the desert and as I retraced my footsteps, my companion was the poem by Robert Browning Hamilton, "Along the Road":

> *I walked a mile with Pleasure.*
> *She chattered all the way,*
> *But left me none the wiser*
> *For all she had to say.*
>
> *I walked a mile with Sorrow,*
> *And ne'er a word said she;*
> *But, oh, the things I learned from her*
> *When Sorrow walked with me!*

I ordered a little stone heart as a marker for Gertie's grave. I knew that her name would go unheeded but I hoped a casual passer-by would pause for a moment to pay tribute to the unknown girl who inspired the simple legend I had inscribed on the stone: *Who knew Gertie, loved Gertie.*

7

Chicken Soup

AFTER GERTIE'S DEATH, I was ready to quit the scene of such an unequal fight, but the spirit of the sanatorium and the plight of the patients had by then become too deeply ingrained in my soul. I was now fighting mad about the widespread indifference to a disease that had plagued mankind for centuries, and was grimly determined to do something about making my promises of hope more real.

The absence of definitive treatment for tuberculosis, almost a half-century after its cause and nature had been made known, reminded me of an incident which took place in one of the demolished cities in postwar Europe where I was stationed. A wretched mother had appeared at my headquarters to ask for a chicken. The broth would save her son's life, she said. I accompanied her to one of the tents in which the homeless were lodged and there I found her sixteen-year-old son dying of "consumption." *Chicken soup* as a cure for TB! And yet chicken soup was no more futile than some of the procedures practiced in enlightened America.

For some reason or other the public health agencies here were not overly excited about the TB threat. Ironically enough, when they did eventually develop an interest, more emphasis was placed on combatting TB in cattle than in human beings. I suppose they reasoned that a cow gives milk and so has a greater economic value than a human being. It was true, of course, that the conquest of bovine TB did have a favorable effect on the total fight against the disease, since it succeeded in eradicating a major source of infection. Nevertheless, the mere fact that more consideration was given to tuberculous cows than to tuberculous human beings rubbed me the wrong way.

I was well versed in all phases of the TB problem as a result of extensive reading and close observation; but, after all, I was a layman. All I could hope to do, therefore, was to stimulate the interest of our medical staff in the use of more aggressive procedures against the disease, and goad them into action.

I spent many an hour reading medical histories, in search of a plausible excuse for the overconservative attitude of the medical profession. I found what was probably a partial alibi. The modern, scientific

doctor had to overcome an unsavory legacy. The evolution of the medicine man was riddled with super-
stition, fakery, and black magic and, even then, there
were some who would commercialize the profession.
To counteract those unethical practices and to deter
the quacks from preying on the sick, the ethical practitioners tended to lean over backwards in their con-
servatism. Under those circumstances, caution could
be considered only a virtue. But when the medical
codes became so rigid and inflexible that they discouraged the introduction of new procedures which
might have had merit, then the price of that virtue was
too high.

It was ten years before the medical profession put
credence in Koch's discovery, probably one of the
greatest boons to mankind, and it was almost twenty
years before the fact that the disease was infectious
filtered down to the people. Only then, millions of
lives later, the slow process of building sanatoria for
the isolation of the tuberculous began, barely in time
to prevent the disease from becoming epidemic
throughout the United States.

My first hospital experience influenced my attitude
toward the need for radical action under critical circumstances and I developed a decided antipathy for
overconservatism, especially when human life was at
stake.

Back in my early immigrant days, when I was just

seventeen years old, I was the "guinea pig" for a new surgical procedure. Not too long after an acquaintance of mine died of appendicitis, I suddenly developed symptomatic pains. Normally, I would have ignored the "bellyache," severe as it was, but the vividness of my friend's recent death prompted me to investigate.

The Rush Medical College, in Chicago, was "only" ten blocks from where I lived so despite a high fever I walked the distance. Almost before I knew it, I was on the operating table undergoing surgery for what proved to be a burst appendix.

In those days, many people did not survive even simple appendectomies and mortality was probably close to one hundred per cent in cases like mine. But I was lucky. The surgeon saw fit to employ a new technique. I had reason to believe it was still in the experimental stage because I was wheeled into an amphitheatre almost every day of my thirty-day stay in the hospital and the surgeon proudly expounded the technique he had used to a gallery of medical students.

Two other circumstances of that hospital stay gave me my first inklings of the vitally important doctor-patient and nurse-patient relationships, especially as they relate to patients who must accept free medical services.

Though I was a poor immigrant boy, the nurses went out of their way to make me feel at ease and even took turns tutoring me in the English language.

The surgeon's kindly attitude toward me also manifested itself strikingly when I told him that I would have to pay his fee a little at a time. "Don't worry, young man," he said. "When you get rich send me twenty-five dollars." I could not foresee, then, that such humanitarianism would vanish as a virtue in years to come.

8

An Oasis

In order to implement a more effective fight against TB, we took steps to build up a medical and scientific staff that would be interested in, and competent to employ, more advanced techniques. To encourage a more aggressive approach, we also needed better facilities and modern equipment. I was fortunate in enlisting the interest of two Good Samaritans in the motion picture industry. One financed the construction and equipment of a new medical building, and the other made new housing facilities available on the grounds for our medical and scientific personnel. A labor union provided the wherewithal for the building of new quarters which housed about thirty-five nurses.

We were also on the lookout for independent investigators who were willing and able to concentrate their efforts on TB research. We housed one doctor and his thousands of mice for almost two years before we were convinced that the trail he was following led nowhere. But we kept right on trying.

Landscaping of the grounds was another important project that got under way about that time. It was not a mere matter of planting trees and flowers, however. The sandy, arid terrain had to be covered by topsoil and every handful of it had to be hauled in from miles away. We were always on the lookout for excavation activities. Sometimes we paid a nominal price for the dirt but more often it was given to us for nothing. Little by little, we hauled in enough earth to make planting possible.

Irrigation was also a major problem. Water was scarce in the area at that time and as nearby citrus growers began to abandon their orchards in favor of more improved sites, we purchased their water rights. In that way, we eventually acquired a sufficient flow of water to further our landscaping program.

A lot of work and discouragement attended the effort, but in time the desert bloomed and was literally transformed into an oasis. Flowers began to grow around the cottages housing the patients and as I made my rounds I could bring color and beauty into the patients' rooms with a single flower or a bouquet plucked from our own flower beds.

Financing the improvement of the grounds was a big worry for a while but as time passed more and more people grew interested in providing gardens, shaded bowers, and spacious green lawns for the benefit of the patients. The initial efforts, however, were planned and paid for by the Junk Peddlers Protective Association of Los Angeles. Yes, junk peddlers, whose daily lives were devoid of beauty, satisfied their own yearnings for the aesthetic by making it available for others. Such were the amazing people who created a desert oasis for their less fortunate fellow men.

The gradual improvement of the physical aspect of the sanatorium was a source of pride for all those associated with its development, but close association with the patients remained the thing dearest to my heart. I wrote letters for them, helped make out their pitiful Last Wills and Testaments, communicated with and consoled their relatives.

We had also managed to establish a "Patients' Fund" by salvaging and selling burlap bags, fats, and other marketable waste. Those who lacked funds for the purchase of small personal items were given "pin money" in a sealed envelope. None knew its source, and none was subjected to prying interrogation to determine whether or not the pittance was justified. That was another unorthodox practice of the sanatorium—a departure from the investigations engaged in by some of the more dogmatic social service agencies, so demeaning to the patients.

The phase of my work, dealing with the preservation of the dignity of the patients, presented many problems. As accommodations became available, the number of patients increased and there was a steady influx of new professional, clerical, and maintenance personnel. Some of them—both old and new—did not hesitate to belittle the patients by reminding them that they were receiving free care. In answer to some reasonable complaint by a patient, I had overheard staff members snap, "What do you want for nothing?" or words to that effect. Whenever it came to my attention that staff members took that attitude toward the patients, they never had another opportunity to pile more grief on those suffering people, because I discharged them on the spot!

My reaction to this attitude reached almost fanatical proportions. I insisted that all personnel—lay and professional alike—subscribe to and practice our humanitarian ideals. I was determined to keep in our service only those who were motivated by a deep humanitarian impulse—personnel who understood the importance of gentle, kind, and considerate care.

The founders and supporters of the sanatorium believed in that concept and were willing to work and sacrifice in order to maintain it. I felt that it was my duty, therefore, to outlaw the use of the term "charity" in relation to our services and to replace it with the benevolent belief that "I *am* my brother's keeper."

It was also necessary to retrain our social service workers and investigators in a pattern peculiarly suited to our unique philosophy. Pauperism was *not* a prerequisite for admission to the sanatorium. On the contrary, we encouraged our patients to hold fast to their meager possessions so they would not be destitute when they left the hospital. Furthermore, we believed that the home and family were the foundation of our civilization and the source of individual happiness. By providing free services, therefore, we not only relieved the patients of financial worry but we were also instrumental in preserving the unity of the home. To most of our patients, that knowledge was as important a contribution to recovery as any of the medical or surgical help they received.

Our philosophy centered around the preservation of human dignity and was contrary to the general concept of charity at that time. Others believed it was not possible, without pampering, to maintain the dignity of those who received free services; that such pampering only encouraged pauperism and malingering. The people of the sanatorium vehemently rejected that interpretation. They were determined that their help for those who were in distress would have no strings attached. They argued that even if a small percentage of the recipients took advantage of their benevolence, it was well worth the price if it prevented the humiliation of the majority.

An Oasis

In recognition of the opportunity given me to maintain the dignity of those who had fallen by the wayside, I coined the slogan which became our watchword:

THERE IS NO PROFIT IN CURING THE BODY
IF, IN THE PROCESS, WE DESTROY THE SOUL

9

A City of Hope

IN THE FIRST PHASE of our program—saving and prolonging the lives of our patients—encouragement began to appear on the horizon in the late twenties when new surgical procedures made their way into the sanatorium. Of little real benefit in effecting cures at first, the mere fact that something new was being tried buoyed the morale of the patients. For the first time, the doctor began to emerge as a factor in the fight against TB, giving rise to the hope that weapons would no longer be confined to rest, good food, fresh air, and sunshine—all within the scope of nature's own function.

One of the techniques was especially radical, requiring the surgical removal of ribs in order to effect a collapse of the diseased lung area. The risk was great and the chances for survival were then approximately one out of five. While I welcomed the

In the beginning . . . two tents (Chapter 2)

Irma, at about three months, and her mother
(Chapter 1)

The author, about 1930 (Chapter 4)

Dora (Chapter 4)

*"Who knew Gertie, loved
Gertie."* (Chapter 6)

Staff and patients about 1929 (Chapter 4)

Dedication of tumor hospital (Chapter 17)

All patients are housed on the ground floor. (Chapter 14)

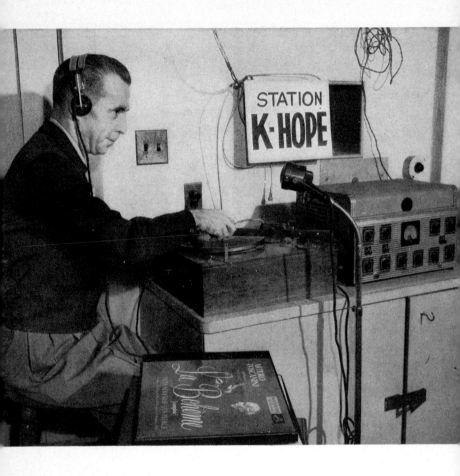

Intercommunication system over which religious services for all faiths, music, news, and sports programs are broadcast daily

progressive action against the disease, it caused me
untold personal grief. The patients had confidence in
me and as their friend and advisor I was brought
into the picture. Eligibility for the operation was of
course established by the professional medical staff.
When they gave the go ahead, it was my duty to see
that patients were mentally and spiritually prepared
for the ordeal ahead. There was always the question
of whether or not they were willing to take the risk
and only the daring gave consent.

When the moment came for the trip to the operating room, there was an end to bravado. It was too
late, then, for pretense. An exchange of glances could
not hide the question uppermost in their minds.
Which would it be? Life or death. Their courage
was magnificent. I was the one who often had to
fight down an overwhelming impulse to run after the
cart shouting, "Don't!"

The hours of waiting were real torture. If all went
according to schedule, the operation took about four
hours—two hundred and forty endless minutes.
Would the surgeon emerge from the operating room
smiling? Or would he be shaking his head from side
to side, eyes downcast? Even when the patient survived the initial shock of the surgery, more anxious
days of watchful waiting lay ahead, more days before
the critical stage had passed, before survival could
be anticipated and hope took on substance. If the

patient survived the surgery and precarious stages of recuperation, he was, for all intents and purposes, cured.

This risky surgical procedure became the subject of frequent and often heated discussions among our doctors. Those who sponsored the radical technique argued that the patients selected for surgery were doomed to die in any event, and that one chance in five was a favorable risk for people in that category. They were also of the opinion that as knowledge and surgical skill increased the mortality rate would decrease. In the face of an eighty per cent mortality at that time, the more progressive staff doctors dared to suggest that surgery might be the long-sought answer to the TB problem. Their predictions were well founded. The mortality rate of that procedure, later perfected and widely practiced, was reduced to less than one per cent.

On the other side were the doctors who argued that there was no sure yardstick for determining whether candidates for surgery were definitely doomed; that there were no reliable statistics justifying the anticipation of even a twenty per cent survival rate. They felt that nature's four-pronged defense against the disease might, in some instances, effect a spontaneous cure among those given the prerogative of surgery. Finally, they insisted that the operation itself was cruel and inhuman.

Sitting in on these discussions, talking with medical men, and reading scanty releases about the new technique, it was my impression that the medical profession was about equally divided at that time on the highly controversial question. I had to acknowledge that the price was high but to me it offered a ray of hope for the future. It was radical but it was constructive; it was action versus inaction and when surgery was indicated, I was usually in favor of it. There was at least as much justification, it seemed to me, for a person who was otherwise doomed to die of a disease to risk a surgical experiment that might save his life and, at the same time, advance medical knowledge, as for healthy young men to risk almost certain death for the sake of gaining a doubtful military advantage in war.

Be that as it may, gradually and steadily a greater percentage of the patients were being discharged and restored to their families. The general public, the medical profession, and health agencies began to recognize the importance of an early diagnosis of the disease and became more alert for symptoms. The JCRA had established a free outpatient clinic in Los Angeles to encourage early diagnosis and also for the purpose of keeping a close check on the immediate families of its in-patients.

The growing number of discharged patients presented a problem of rehabilitation. Here, again, the supporters of the sanatorium rose to the need. A home for ex-patients was established in Los Angeles where they were separated from the hospital environment but remained under careful supervision. Their activities were gradually increased and they were taught new trades more compatible with their strength. Eventually restored mentally, physically, and spiritually, ex-patients of our little sanatorium became self-supporting, contributing members of society.

At long last hope began to take on a semblance of reality and my conscience was no longer sorely troubled by the continual need to build up false hopes. Hope was more real now and the seed of that new hope took root and was to blossom into—A CITY OF HOPE!

10

The Battle of Life

THE UNITED STATES had shed its swaddling clothes during the First World War and, after the armistice, emerged as a nation whose economic, political, and military power merited the respect of the world. Unfortunately, President Wilson's dream of a League of Nations had been shattered by those who held to outmoded tradition, and the war which was fought "to make the world safe for democracy" only set the stage for totalitarianism. It had also ushered in an era of lawlessness, intense nationalism based on a rivalry for territorial boundaries, and a greedy materialism.

In my travels throughout Eastern Europe after the war, I had been staggered by the utter demoralization and degradation of the people there as a result of four years of war and the reign of terror which was its aftermath. Respect for human life and the dignity of the individual was regarded as a show of Western weakness by the new tyrants who browbeat their subjects into submission by the artful use of mental and physical torture.

I was not especially surprised to find that the inhumanity from which I had fled to the United States some twenty years before still prevailed in a country that had incubated such humanitarians as Ivan the Terrible, Peter the so-called Great, Rasputin, and so many others of that same ilk. But I was at a complete loss to understand why the people continued to tolerate such mental and physical slavery in that enlightened era. Even worse, the end was not in sight. Everywhere I went, I saw the terrible agony caused by the evil legacies which had been preserved intact and practiced by one generation after another. Almost every night, the roar and backfire of racing truck motors struck fear into the hearts of the people. They knew the noise was a cover for the machine-gun fusillades that toppled long rows of human beings into the trenched graves they themselves had been forced to dig.

A true story, told to me by an eyewitness, revealed the insidious means used by these madmen to build up the fear that brought people to their knees. The daughter of a respected local family was courted by a comparative newcomer to the village who had won their confidence and admiration. They became con-

cerned about his safety because of the fearless way
he spoke out against the oppressors. Not long after
the family and friends of his fiancée developed the
courage to nod in mute agreement with his views,
the racing truck motors sounded their death knell.
Yes, the girl's sweetheart was an instrument of the
Bolsheviki and it had been his deliberate mission to
encourage the villagers to express resentment against
the regime. Complete silence, and the ability to control facial muscles, therefore, became the only pro-
tection against trumped-up charges. Possibly, this
accounts for the deadpan expression of Eastern European diplomats and military men, even today.

In terms of dollars and cents, times were good in
the United States and the people were busy chasing
their favorite phantoms—too busy to notice or pro-
test too much the anguish of their fellow man in other
parts of the world. Our intense concentration on the
technological arts had earned us the reputation of
being a materialistic people who had no talent for the
creation of permanent spiritual and cultural values.
Even as we pointed with pride to the high standard
of living enjoyed by the common people of our nation,
we were given a look at ourselves as others saw us
when a New York City newspaper carried the con-
clusions of a Chinese scholar who had ostensibly made
a thorough study of our American institutions. It was
his considered opinion that if a great catastrophe were

to wipe the United States and all of its people off the face of the earth, our only legacy for posterity would be the poem "Annabel Lee" by Edgar Allen Poe. It remained for history to prove or disprove his prognosis.

The unprecedented industrial and economic growth in the United States was still booming when in 1929 newspaper headlines a foot high heralded the great stock market crash. The worst depression in our nation's history was on.

When months stretched into years and prosperity stubbornly refused to "turn the corner," the financial status of the City of Hope began to mirror the dreary national scene. By 1932, our situation had become ominous. Indebtedness was upward of two hundred thousand dollars, six months' pay was due most of the staff, and all purchases were on a cash-on-delivery basis.

At this crucial point, our then executive director, whose primary function was to obtain financial support for the sanatorium, decided to call it a day. The job of saving our work and our dreams was handed to me. I was warned that it could not be done but I was not ready to give up without making an all-out effort to save what seemed to me the one sane spot in a world gone mad. I might not have had the courage to tackle the task ahead if I had not been blinded to its magnitude by an overwhelming sense of personal responsibility for the welfare of the patients and a driving desire to preserve the human values fostered and practiced at the City of Hope.

The sanatorium had been my world for over six years. I knew every phase of its operation, its problems, and the actions and reactions of the people who were fighting a battle *for* life. Now I was faced with an entirely different challenge, involving a nation-wide base and work with distressed people who were preoccupied with the battle *of* life.

The first jolt came with the realization that I would have to give up the two pursuits I had come to cherish most—the close relationship with the patients and the long nights devoted to reading and reflection. But saving the hospital for the patients had become my first consideration and, with a heavy heart, I began to taper off my work at the sanatorium. Finally I left its confines altogether, and made my headquarters in Los Angeles.

I had not been concerned with fund-raising activities beyond the immediate limits of the sanatorium before, and had no knowledge of professional fund-raising techniques. Before I could determine how support could be increased and accelerated I had to familiarize myself with and appraise our current sources of income and the methods by which support was obtained. In addition, it was vitally important to develop an approach to those elements in our society which had failed to rally to our cause before.

Of necessity, my campaign had to be built on a weak and unstable base. I was faced with the task of selling a program dedicated to the saving of human life and human dignity to a world which no longer seemed to place any value on those commodities. The political restlessness on the international scene, the long shadows cast by totalitarianism in various parts of the world, and the severe depression in our own land had brought about a general breakdown in the moral fiber of man. People were grasping for any ideological straws, of domestic or foreign origin, that gave promise of stabilizing their tottering world. They seemed to me to be groping for something to fill the spiritual vacuum in their lives, and imbued with a sense of mission I decided to base my campaign on the plea for a return to "man's humanity to man."

The going was tough. I appealed to old friends and acquaintances who I thought might be willing to offer us a helping hand, and I traveled extensively to seek out and interview prospective patrons in all walks of life. My days became an endless routine of train schedules and appointments. Because of the philanthropic nature of my work, I received free passes for train trips. They usually provided accommodations on second-class trains but that proved to be an advantage. The long rides on slow trains gave me time to reflect

on the day's victories and defeats and to make my
plans for the scheduled activities ahead.

Making speeches before large groups became my
personal nightmare. It was a new experience and obviously required qualifications I did not possess. I had
long been an admirer of great oratory and had even
studied the technique of the notable speechmakers of
history, but at the psychological moment the know-
how deserted me. I began to feel that unless I learned
to transmit my message effectively, my campaign for
support would be doomed to failure. I became ultra-
sensitive about my deficiencies as an orator and the
hours preceding each meeting were filled with torture, the hours after with discouragement.

One evening after I had addressed a group of auxiliary members and their friends, one of the women
suggested that my talk left much to be desired. I said,
meekly, "I'm sorry, but that is the best I can do." As
I retreated in embarrassment, the president of the
group caught up with me. Hoping to soften the blow
to my pride, she said, "Don't let that woman's opinion upset you. She's a little off and just repeats what
she hears others say!"

Only my fanatical devotion to the cause gave me
the courage to keep on subjecting myself to that kind
of grief and embarrassment. I never succeeded in
overcoming the handicap but I took courage from the

fact that the earnestness of my appeal began to produce results and even brought me through most of the meetings more or less successfully. In studying the lives of men and women who had been instrumental in the creation of notable enterprises throughout history, I was surprised to discover that many of them admitted to being almost inarticulate when they came face to face with a large audience. It followed, then, that oratory was not a prerequisite for accomplishment and I came to realize that what was said was more vital to the achievement of end results than how it was said. That realization freed me from my bugaboo once and for all and I decided to follow the example of wiser heads and leave the oratory for those who were not so preoccupied with finding solutions for our immediate problems.

My first appeals were directed to women because the greatest measure of our support up to that time had initiated with them. In reflecting on that fact, I decided that their marked interest in saving and preserving life was a transference of the maternal instinct innate in the female who, from time immemorial, had been the procreator and defender of life. But in addition to their natural inclination for humanitarian work, there were other factors which governed their choice of group affiliations. One of the considerations was prestige and, up to that time, membership in our auxiliaries promised little if any social recognition.

Based on my appraisal of the times, however, I decided that women in the upper social cliques had begun to think less in terms of prestige and more in terms of values. The depression had curtailed their chase after the phantoms which had occupied their leisure hours, and I wooed them with the concept that "Man cannot live by bread alone," promising spiritual nourishment and personal gratification from active participation in our humanitarian program. I must have struck a responsive chord because a number of women in the higher income brackets began to form auxiliaries for the City of Hope.

At the same time, I also succeeded in enlisting the interest of the younger generation and we soon had a fair number of "Junior" groups. The mothers were especially delighted with the fact that their daughters—most of them members of the so-called "Lost Generation"—were demonstrating a sense of responsibility toward themselves and others.

Next came the men. Up until that time, auxiliary membership was made up almost entirely of women. But the depression had set a lot of men back on their heels. They had learned a hard lesson in the precariousness of material possessions. I decided that they, too, were in need of an activity that did not use the dollar as a yardstick. Unlike women, however, the men at first failed to respond naturally to the humanitarian approach and I had to use a different key to unlock their sympathies. I found it in a masculine trait I had often observed when showing visitors around the sanatorium. Time and again I had seen business tycoons, who would stop at nothing to gain their ends in a competitive world, become expansive in the presence of the sick and helpless who could not meet them on equal terms.

In addition to the fact that this characteristic was the "Open Sesame" to their support, it also made me feel there was still hope for the human race. When the lower animal sees another weak and helpless, he attacks with greater ferocity. Most human beings, on the other hand, are inclined to help those weaker than themselves. I played on that human trait to enlist the interest of the men, and all-male auxiliaries have since become a vital factor in support of the City of Hope.

The third phase of our program dealt with an approach to labor. For many years, the worker had been the recipient of professional philanthropy in time of need. He had always viewed such sources of help with aversion because they were administered with complete indifference for his individual problems. During the depression, that bounty tapered off, assumed the aspect of a handout, and became an even more bitter pill to swallow than before.

When the New Deal presented the workers with a Magna Charta, collective bargaining was given a boost. The unions mushroomed, and the economic lot of the wage earners improved considerably. I felt that the time had come, therefore, for labor to take care of its own in the field of health as well as on the economic front. We stressed the fact that in providing highly specialized medical care, free of cost to our patients, the City of Hope made every possible effort to preserve the dignity of the individual.

As the collective bargaining machinery began to work more smoothly, the cares of the labor leader lessened. He had more freedom and, having become public-relations conscious, welcomed the opportunity to sit with management around conference tables to discuss mutual cooperation in humanitarian enterprises. Labor responded generously to my appeals for support, and through the years has continued to play an important role in the development and support of the City of Hope.

For two years, I kept going at a pace requiring almost superhuman stamina, defining, evaluating, and translating all these factors in our society into support for our cause. Little by little my efforts began to bring results. But even as the sanatorium began to pulsate with a degree of new vigor, evidencing a new lease on life, the long hours and tensions began to demand their price. I broke down and it was three months before I regained my equilibrium. The price was worth paying, however, because it seemed that, after all, our City of Hope and the human values manifested there could be saved.

11

Women

OUR AUXILIARIES—and the term was synonymous
with "women" at that time—operated on a propor-
tionate mixture of "cause" and "social activity," and
as I traveled around the country, I attended innumer-
able social functions devoted to fund-raising activities in behalf of the sanatorium.

I met and worked with many women during that
critical period, but my interest in them as individuals was in direct proportion to the efforts they were
willing to expend in support of the City of Hope.

The hectic pattern of my life excluded entanglements. Believing that "He travels fastest who travels
alone," I had always guarded my bachelorhood jeal-
ously, lest marriage come between me and the
achievement of my aims and objectives.

Furthermore, I had had an opportunity in my
youth to observe the institution of marriage in both
Oriental and Occidental cultures and was impressed

with neither. The complete domination of the female by the male in the Orient, and the trend toward complete domination of the male by the female in the Occident, indicated a lack of balance in the relationship which I chose to avoid.

Some of my best friends were married, however, and it seemed to be their sole mission in life to separate me from my single status. Feeling the need to build up a sound defense in order to be able to parry their more telling arguments, I turned to my always reliable source of information—books. The discourses on marriage were enlightening and I was especially gratified to learn that they bore out many of my own convictions.

It had long been my contention that marriage was contrary to the fundamental laws of nature, as they related to the perpetuation of life. Man himself instigated the partnership between male and female for an entirely different purpose. As his mental processes had improved through the ages, his perception of life deepened and he became aware of the fact that, individually, his stay on this planet was transitory. Having developed an ego in the meantime, he began to feel concerned over the perpetuation of his name and possessions. Eventually, he hit on a logical means toward that end—sole ownership of a female and continuation of his bloodline through the offspring.

In the execution of that plan the male was at a disadvantage. Both the male and female of the species were polygamous by nature and practice, and the role of the male was comparatively insignificant in the total process of propagation. To implement his purpose he found it necessary to propose a partnership with a female of his choice, committing himself to the provision of food, clothing, and shelter, for her and the children which he—and he alone—would sire.

In the beginning, the marriage contract called for the practice of monogamy by the female only, since that served the intent of the dominant male. But since polygamy was as natural to her as it was to him, she grew restive under that one-sided restraint and began to struggle for equality. The extent to which the marriage contract imposed the practice of monogamy on both sexes, in the various cultures throughout the world, was in direct ratio to the progress made by the female in achieving equality with the male on that scene.

Since I firmly believed that the evolution of the family unit was one of the major forces in accelerating man's climb toward a higher level of civilization, I was, of course, heartily in favor of marriage, home, and family—for everyone but myself. In formulating the City of Hope program I had stated emphatically that the home was the basis of our civilization and that the family was the source of our happiness. For one thing, they exemplified one of the primary tenets in our philosophy—that every one could, by making a conscious effort, overcome the innate drives which testified to the relatively short distance man had traveled from his animal beginnings. It was not always easy but it could be done. There were many evidences of man's conscious and conscientious efforts to control and even change the animal characteristics which still clung to him. For instance, the male of the species had to develop a love for his offspring, since originally the instinct was innate only to the female. But both male and female had succeeded in retaining an affinity for their progeny long after they became self-reliant and even from generation to generation.

In the course of my work with the members of our Women's Auxiliaries, I learned to view their unique problems with a more sympathetic eye. Since it was, and in most instances still is, the prerogative of the male to propose a partnership, the female practiced certain artful ruses to decoy the male into a proposal of marriage. I had ample opportunity to observe the effectiveness of some of their courtship practices and considered myself an authority on the subject. That knowledge served two very important purposes. First, recognizing them for what they were, I was prepared to counteract any overtures, and second, convinced that the home and family—natural outgrowths of marriage—were the basis for building a better society, I felt qualified—and justified—in acting as a coach for prospective homemakers who had not yet mastered the artifices of courtship.

My star pupil was a demure little Canadian miss who was a comparative newcomer to our cause. She was an ardent worker, and, despite a natural shyness, excelled in fund-raising activities. We met often as a result of our mutual interests, and I came to appreciate her sympathetic understanding of the overwhelming problems I had encountered in trying to save the City of Hope from financial ruin. I was a confirmed bachelor, of course, so I decided to help her find a husband who would appreciate her obvious qualifications as a wife and mother. She lacked the aggressiveness to practice the courting stratagems which, to me, seemed the most appealing, so I offered my services as a tutor.

The effectiveness of my teaching ability and her aptness as a pupil were demonstrated on January 20, 1934, when I found myself standing at her side before a judge in Las Vegas, meekly parroting, "I do."

Contrary to all my fears that marriage would interfere with my work, my wife's serenity under fire and her tolerance for my obvious eccentricities became a stabilizing influence in my life. She also possessed an almost uncanny knack for knowing just when my morale needed bolstering. Yes, I became convinced that marriage at its best was a good influence on human progress.

12

Antibiotic

I HAD NO SOONER begun to feel confident that our
struggle to save the City of Hope was an accomplished fact, than we came face to face with the
realization that nothing could be certain in an uncertain world.

On the German scene, the barbaric spirit had
again broken through its thin veneer of Western civilization and the horrors perpetrated by the totalitarian regime in that arena stole the stage from the
more humanitarian practices on the American scene.
The people of the West became even more confused,
mentally and spiritually, when they awoke to the possibility that Naziism and its unique brand of inhumanity threatened to take over their world. The
outlook for the free peoples became desperate when
Germany and Russia joined forces, obliterating the
faint ray of hope that their long-standing distrust of

one another would bring them to grips and prove the seed of their ultimate destruction.

During a two-year sojourn in Germany in the early twenties, I had seen the struggle there between Communism and the Socialism of the Weimar government. Marching in opposite directions, adherents of the opposing ideologies paraded on the same street. Both conformed to the accepted standards of German discipline and both were equally unaware that the same propensity for regimentation was brewing another ideology, in a Munich beer cellar, which was to destroy them both on that scene and for a time threaten every other ideology in the world.

Chauvinism and a seething nationalism were manifested in "border incidents"—each a potential powder keg. It was no novelty to read in the newspapers that the young Polish nation, only recently freed from many decades of political enslavement, was following the example of its former oppressors, grabbing land from neighboring countries and tyrannizing its own people.

When these greedy instincts culminated in the Second World War, the degraded physical, moral, and ethical standards advocated by the totalitarian movements gave rise to horrors never before perpetrated on, or experienced by, mankind. For six long years a large segment of the people on this earth were reveling in murder for murder's sake and cruelty for cruelty's sake, taking sadistic delight in violating every precept of human decency. In his long climb upward from bestiality, man had lost his footing many times before, but he had never before sunk back so low. The question was whether he would continue his descent toward the animal, losing all his human attributes on the way, or whether he would find enough spiritual strength to dig in once again and start working his way back, building a better human society.

In the face of this degenerative process, I was traveling the length and breadth of the land, preaching "man's humanity to man" as it was practiced at our sanatorium, pointing out that as human life became cheaper throughout the world it grew more precious at the City of Hope. My appeals attracted those who had not lost all hope in man's ability to reverse his course and strive for a nobler destiny.

When the Second World War ended, in 1945, and the immediate threat of the totalitarian evil was subdued, hope for a better world began to rise again in the human breast. Here and there I began to see evidence that man had had his fill of the wholesale destruction of human life and was growing alarmed over the overt display of malice and ill will. As people became more receptive to the idea that saving life was a more human attribute than its destruction, they began to scan the horizon for signs of a better day. They seemed to be groping for something that could purge and restore their ravaged spirits.

Convinced that the services and human values inherent in the City of Hope program were at least the seeds for a spiritual force which would prove equal to the needs of the new day, I wondered how I could make these values known to more people.

On the long train trips, away from the immediate concern about bread and butter for the sanatorium, I began to analyze our program, dissect it, and place each component in its logical sphere. I began to dream of building a greater City of Hope—a Medical Center which would embody more far-reaching opportunities for humanitarian service and practices, and so bring about a greater awareness of its philosophy. We could then offer more people an opportunity for direct and personal participation in good work—the most effective "antibiotic" yet developed for a sick and debilitated spirit.

Always I realized that self-interest was man's first consideration. He asked, logically enough, "If I am not for myself, who will be?" It was only on second thought that the question arose: "If I am for myself only, what am I?" On that premise, I had to find a way to engender unselfishness by playing on man's interest in benefiting himself.

A lesson I had learned early in life provided a clue. As a lad in Russia, I was one of several boys in our small village who attended classes held at regular intervals by an itinerant religious instructor. He was a devout man and conscientious in his efforts to teach Judaic concepts to his young charges.

The sessions were long and our interest was short. At the first signs of restlessness, he would give us fair warning that we would suffer for our misdeeds and, furthermore, that punishment would be visited upon us here on this earth. The fact that he was quoting from Mosaic Law gave the threat substance. But he always gave us an alternative from the same source. "If you do good on this earth, you will receive your reward in this life." I can still remember the sobering effect of his closing statement: "It is up to you." The realization that I was the captain of my own fate made me think twice about risking retaliation for misdemeanors.

Though our instruction had religious overtones, the lessons dealt primarily with fundamental laws and incentives for leading a good life on this earth. Little time was given to conjecture about the immortality of the body or soul, or to the promise of reward and hazard of punishment after death.

As years passed, the idea that man must look to himself for the fulfillment of his spiritual destiny took on greater significance. The various reservoirs from which he had drawn his spiritual nourishment for centuries began to recede as science persisted in widening his mental and physical horizons. It became evident that another source of supply which would be more compatible with his new and realistic concepts of life was needed to fill that vacuum.

When I finally had the medical center clearly blueprinted in my mind, I felt more than ever that in enlarging the scope of our services we could satisfy both of the entities within man—the spiritual as well as the physical. Our functional program which was dedicated to the saving and prolonging of human life would serve man's physical self, and personal participation in furthering that humanitarian objective would fortify and strengthen his spiritual self.

Furthermore, people would have a selfish interest for participating in our broader program. In addition to benefiting physically and spiritually, it seemed logical that if they could anticipate spiritual rewards on this earth, life would become more precious and our objective of helping them round out their allotted span would therefore gain in stature.

The thought of creating a City of Hope Medical Center was rarely out of my mind. I convinced myself that we, the people of the City of Hope, could and would create the first medical center on the American scene to have the unique objective of adding "life to years" as well as "years to life."

13

"Golter's Folly"

WAR, ACCIDENT, AND DISEASE were still the foremost threats to man's comparatively short span of life on this earth. Of these three, disease took the greatest toll.

I had reasoned that it was not within the realm of probability that we, the people of the City of Hope, could prevent war or control accidents to any appreciable extent, but that it was reasonable to hope that we could become a vital factor in the fight against disease.

In formulating my plans for converting the sanatorium into a more comprehensive medical center, I visualized that our functional and ideological program would be built on three pillars: Service, Humanitarianism, and Reward. By expanding the phase of our program which was more readily understood—

the saving of human life by virtue of our specialized services—we would be able to interest and indoctrinate larger numbers of people in the philosophy supported by the other two pillars—humanitarianism and reward. The fact that we already had an army of dedicated workers, seasoned warriors in support of that fight, was a definite advantage.

But we were confronted with perplexing problems which had affected the large majority of our supporters. Six million Jews had been annihilated in the European cataclysm and, with them, the centers of Jewish spiritual and cultural life. The inconceivable brutalities inflicted on innocent people had given rise to despair in the American Jewish community. Many had lost faith in mankind and in human values. It seemed that the unremitting persecution accepted by the Jews throughout the centuries in the interest of preserving the Judaic concept of moral and ethical codes had been in vain. Some contended—and with logic—that since those values which had been promulgated to humanize mankind had come to nothing, further sacrifice for the sake of their preservation was unwarranted. Voices grew stronger in favor of relaxing the dogged determination of the Jews to maintain their identity as a people.

I did not share those opinions or the prevalent defeatism. Disturbed by such developments I withdrew, temporarily, from my immediate activities in order to evaluate the trend and its possible effects on an institution operated under Jewish auspices.

I, too, had been shocked by the return to bestiality of those who had conceived the genocidal atrocities against the Jews and by the indifference of so many people toward these manifestations. But I had not lost faith in the basic worth of Judaic concepts. While it was true that some elements of the human race still reverted to animal brutality, it was equally true that all people had not reached the higher levels of human behavior. Hope lay in the fact that man had at least acquired the capacity to realize it when he was headed in the wrong direction, and that he made an effort to reverse his course.

At any rate, it seemed to me that a people who had given the human race the greatest moral and ethical pattern for advancing civilization, as well as so many spiritual stepping stones, including mono-theism, was justified in retaining its ethnic identity at all costs. I reasoned that the Jews as a people had not yet run their full course, and that their further contributions to human society would be richer if cut from the fabric of their singular heritage.

The destruction of the centers in Europe from which the Jews had siphoned their ancestral iden-tification and spiritual strength had, in my opinion, only magnified the need for rebuilding them in the United States—in a country which encouraged and drew strength from its plural heritage. I felt that we could contribute to the enrichment of the American scene and at the same time preserve our identity as a people by creating institutions which would be operated under Jewish auspices on a broad nonsectarian basis. It followed that in building a greater City of Hope, we would be blazing a trail in that direction.

As my plans for the medical center began to take shape, I put out feelers in order to get reactions to so ambitious an undertaking. Generally speaking, the response was not encouraging. A few were in favor of the project because its magnitude appealed to their pioneering spirits. Others claimed it was biting off too much for humble people to swallow, and still others shrugged it off as "Golter's Folly."

Not to be discouraged, however, I spent twelve months drafting plans for the functional program of a medical center which would embody hospitals and clinics staffed and equipped to diagnose and treat major diseases on the same free basis that had been the policy of the original tuberculosis sanatorium. It would also include a research division manned by leading scientists who would concentrate on finding causes and cures for the specific diseases treated in our hospitals, an undergraduate and post-graduate medical school, teaching facilities for medical technicians, and a nurses' training school.

On May 1, 1946, my plans for the medical center

were submitted to a special Medical Advisory Committee for study. On May 8, they were favorably recommended to the Board of Directors by that committee. On May 27, the Board went on record as approving the program in principle, and I was authorized to prepare the plan for presentation to the national convention. On July 10, the Board approved the final draft for presentation to the convention, adding their recommendation for its adoption. On July 16, the Medical Advisory Board of the sanatorium unanimously approved the program.

But the real test was yet to come. It still had to be ratified by the Convention. Delegates, representing the sundry groups in whose hands lay the policy-making power and full authority for governing our institution, convened on August 1, 1946. On the first day, the consensus seemed to be that the project was too big—beyond all reason for humble people. I pointed out that big things could be done in this world with "the few dollars of the many, rather than with the many dollars of the few." Nevertheless, the proposition was on the verge of being defeated when one of its proponents moved that the vote be deferred to the next day's session.

I spent the entire night preparing a new series of resolutions, breaking the plan down into separate segments. By presenting it in smaller units, I hoped to salvage at least some parts of the program. In

order to allay any fears that we might overextend
ourselves financially, I drew up a resolution which
read: "The process of growth shall not exceed the
development of support, and the making of loans
to promote any part of this enterprise shall be pro-
hibited." That was contrary to the pattern established
by the founders—that we build first and worry about
funds later—but at that point I was willing to com-
promise in order to gain approval for my dream.

During the long night, I had also managed to line
up some of the delegates who were in sympathy with
the program. I felt that their objective arguments
in its favor would carry more weight than mine. The
Medical Center Program was presented to the Convention the next day again, this time embodied in
twelve separate resolutions. I sat tense and mute on
the platform during the lengthy and heated debates,
hoping against hope that at least some of the points
would be ratified. They were voted on one by one
and the session continued for hours. But when the
final gavel fell, each resolution in turn had been
adopted unanimously. The Convention had given
us the mandate. All we had to do was fulfill it.

14

Dreams versus Dollars

THE MANDATE GIVEN US by the Convention was only the first step toward the creation of our Medical Center. We were faced with the huge task of transforming a sanatorium which had been devoted exclusively to the care and treatment of tuberculous patients into an institution which was to incorporate facilities for the diagnosis and treatment of other major diseases.

Creating the physical facilities to house the contemplated services was a giant undertaking in itself, but their realization within the framework of our defined ideological program presented even greater problems. We worked with various architects for many months but found it difficult to overcome their traditional ideas about hospital construction.

Functionally and aesthetically, the submitted drawings left little to be desired but none met our exacting specifications for the well-being and comfort of the patients. To save space and money, the architects had visualized multi-storied structures which were inconsistent with my theory that patients should be housed only on the main floor where they would be close to the stream of life and enjoy an eye-level view of growing flowers and nature's other bounties. There were to be no wards and each room, with no less than two exposures, was to accommodate no more than two patients.

It soon became evident that if the physical facilities of our new medical center were to be compatible with its ideological program, we would need an architect who understood and could translate our humanitarian concepts into brick and mortar.

We inadvertently found the solution to that particular problem as a result of our efforts to solve another one. Wholesome food was a therapeutic necessity for our patients and their general lack of appetite was a constant worry. In the process of enlarging our scientific staff we had engaged a dietician who was a recent graduate of a California university. Her parents were among the pioneers of the sanatorium and she had been thoroughly indoctrinated with its humanitarian objectives. It was during her tenure that we introduced daily menus from which the patients could order their meals three times a day. Not only were they more inclined to eat the food they had selected voluntarily but, in addition, they derived a spiritual satisfaction from the knowledge that they were given an option.

As it happened, the fiancé of our new dietician was an architect who had only recently started to practice his profession. During his frequent visits to the City of Hope she had succeeded in transmitting her own enthusiasm for its unique philosophy to him. Up to that time he had been concentrating his efforts on residential construction and was not familiar with the highly specialized structural requirements necessary for our contemplated services. But when he showed a sympathetic understanding of our architectural problems, I proposed that he visit and study various hospitals throughout the nation so that he would be able to coordinate our functional facilities with the accommodations we had visualized for the patients.

It turned out to be a happy experiment. Before too long, construction had gotten under way on a number of new facilities and ground was broken for a $2,500,000 central medical building, from which hospital wings and service units were to radiate like the spokes of a wheel.

The young couple, who had married in the meantime, shared their great pride in the buildings which began to materialize under his supervision. But by the time some of the first units in the planned series were nearing completion, our promising young architect was stricken by a critical illness. He died soon after witnessing the dedication of one of the first buildings to come off of his drawing board. The facilities which he had designed became the battleground for a fight against the disease which caused his tragic and untimely death—leukemia.

Obviously, a great institution cannot be built by dreams alone. It takes dollars—and more dollars! It was one thing to interest people in a fight against catastrophic diseases, helping the helpless, and alleviating suffering, and quite another to translate an intangible philosophy into participation and support.

The attainment of the $7,215,000 budget ratified by the 1946 Convention was a sobering thought, even to a perennial optimist like myself. But to those who were faced with the practical considerations of raising that unprecedented figure, the reality was staggering. We were setting out to blaze an uncharted trail, an effort which would require all the courage and stamina we could muster. If we were to reach our goal, new converts had to be won for our program, and new vigor, enthusiasm, and inspiration had to be generated. Here, again, had I known what lay ahead, I might not have had the courage to undertake the task.

But, optimistic as usual, I had predicted in my report to the Convention that by stepping up activities, our national organization could meet the unprecedented two-year budget necessary for the early realization of our goal, "barring unforeseen developments."

In our search for support, the first and most serious of the "unforeseen developments" began to materialize. It was true that the world had been freed from the immediate threat of totalitarianism but the price had been fearful. The dire straits of many victims of World War II could be expressed no better than in the words of an American soldier who stood among the ruins of a French village. As he gazed in dismay at the rubble which he and his buddies had risked so much to retake from the enemy, he was moved to remark: "Boy! We sure liberated the hell out of this place!"

So foreign relief and rehabilitation of the "liberated" people of Europe took the stage and held the spotlight month after month. During that period, which extended into years, interest and support for activities on the home scene, no matter how worthy, were pigeonholed. Not only were vast sums collected and channeled overseas, but the best workers in our own and other organizations had been drafted for that effort.

We began to find it difficult to meet the minimum budgetary requirements for our basic needs and it became necessary to institute drastic economies. We were hard pressed to maintain even our old sources of income and the implementation of the City of Hope Medical Center came to a virtual standstill.

Another "unforeseen development" which hampered our progress was the rapidly spiraling costs of building, maintenance, and operation in the immediate postwar period. Furthermore, in keeping with our policy to give our patients the benefit of the finest available medical and surgical care, we had introduced the use of costly new drugs and specialized equipment for the more effective treatment of TB. Those uncontrolled costs made one day's careful calculations obsolete on the next and certain specific commitments had to be paid for with many more dollars than had been earmarked for them originally.

A third "unforeseen development" was the difficulty we experienced in indoctrinating our own people, as well as the public at large, in the greater implications inherent in our Medical Center program. It was not easy to sell an idea still in the blueprint stage, to make people understand that by broadening the scope of our service we hoped to regenerate a general interest in the return to the moral and ethical values practiced at the City of Hope.

I was convinced, however, that we, the people of the City of Hope, had a "rendezvous with destiny" and that we could keep our tryst with the warm and personal help of "the many" rather than through the cold, impersonal support of "the few." I also believed that people in all walks of life and of all income levels would welcome an opportunity to participate in the building of a great humanitarian institution and that their active participation would be a concrete source of spiritual nourishment.

In the meantime, the "unforeseen developments" made it necessary for us to revise the timetable for the completion of our Medical Center and to redouble our efforts in seeking support. Once again, it fell to me to travel in an attempt to revitalize our auxiliaries and form new ones, while trying to find and develop "apostles" who understood and could translate our philosophy to others. It was a hard road, filled with frustration, but we never faltered in our determination to maintain the highest possible standards of service as we strived to bring our total program into being.

We also held fast to our ideals, as expressed in the words of that great humanitarian, Louis Pasteur:

> We do not ask of an unfortunate, "What country do you come from?" or "What is your religion?" We say to him, "You suffer, that is enough. You belong to us; we shall make you well."

15

A People's Movement

THE OBSTACLES which barred the path of our progress toward the creation of a specialized medical center continued to loom large and menacing. The problem centered on a clear definition of the "People's Movement" which was to be the lifeline of the institution. The question was posed: "Can a People's Movement such as ours build and support a program of such magnitude on a permanent basis?" Based on our past experience, I was convinced that the answer could be in the affirmative. For many years, however, our activities had been keyed to the merciful appeal of caring for sick bed patients. We had to overcome that "sanatorium psychology" and gear our thinking and activities to the broader program.

In the light of our increased budgetary requirements, I tried to think of ways and means by which we could harness the tremendous potential inherent in the various groups which constituted our support.

The auxiliaries, chartered for the purpose of providing continuous support for the City of Hope, were the core of our People's Movement. From the earliest days of the sanatorium, the organization of auxiliaries had been more or less spontaneous. They grew by word of mouth. One person told another about the humanitarian services of the struggling little institution which was dedicated to the fight against disease, and a new auxiliary was born. Enthusiastic members of existing auxiliaries also prodded the interest of friends and relatives and often traveled to distant cities, voluntarily, in order to organize new groups.

The people of the City of Hope always had a sense of personal responsibility toward its welfare and, as a result, our network of auxiliaries had never grown static, a circumstance which was a vital factor in its progressive growth.

Augmenting the efforts of our auxiliaries were fraternal orders, labor and management bodies, business and industrial interests, social groups with leanings for philanthropic causes, and a legion of individuals whose interest and support we had been able to enlist.

Since the chartered auxiliaries constituted the major source of our income, it was necessary to review the incentives which had proved effective in stimulating their efforts in behalf of the City of Hope and to re-evaluate the benefits derived from affiliation with those groups.

Of first importance was the fact that our auxiliaries operated on the principle of "Town Hall" democracy which had been initiated by the pioneers of the sanatorium. Each group was free to determine its own course of action, unhampered by directives from a central office. We found that organized groups thrived on ideas which they themselves originated and showed less enthusiasm for implementing ideas foisted on them. Our auxiliary members also derived a deeper sense of satisfaction from self-instigated activities and, in turn, exerted greater effort toward their realization. In the truest sense, they became dedicated workers and counted their benefits far in excess of the cost in effort and sacrifice.

The longevity of our individual auxiliaries was a credit to the autonomy which encouraged individual initiative. That procedure also served to develop leadership by placing responsibility for the creation and implementation of ideas squarely upon the members themselves. I believed that every human being had the innate desire and capacity for leadership and that those latent talents could be brought to the surface when encouraged.

Extending a helping hand to the sick, pride in the creation of a unique philanthropic enterprise, a social outlet inspired by humanitarian objectives—all were impelling motives for participation in our People's Movement. But the true sense of mission, which gave birth to dedication, welled from the knowledge that in helping others we, the people of the City of Hope, were bellringers for a return to the moral and ethical codes that separated man from beast.

In seeking the most effective procedures for our auxiliary network, we came to realize that the operation of groups on a unit basis was in their best interests as well as that of the City of Hope. Councils, which encouraged cooperative ventures within a given area, tended to nullify the competitive spirit which was vital to sustained interest and productiveness.

The sense of personal participation in the total program of the City of Hope was further enhanced by attendance at the biennial conventions. Duly elected delegates, representing tens of thousands of auxiliary members, got together from all parts of the nation to review the progress made possible through their efforts during the preceding two years, to establish policies for the subsequent two years, elect a governing board, and issue mandates for progressive developments. Representatives of other supporting groups attended the conventions as delegates-at-large, and unaffiliated individuals attended as ambassadors-at-large, each having equal voting status with the auxiliary delegates.

In the alternate years, regional conferences were held which provided a further opportunity for an interchange of ideas, presentation of progress reports and suggestions for accomplishing mutual goals. The delegates returned from those conclaves to their respective cities with the assured knowledge that they were an integral part of that People's Movement, charged with the responsibility of reporting on activities and progress. In turn, they inspired their co-workers to exert their best efforts in giving impetus to the program.

Those were just a few of the considerations vital to a cause which depended on a People's Movement for moral and financial support. They were the basis of an honest effort to evaluate and create incentives and rewards for those who devoted time and effort in support of the City of Hope.

While the "unforeseen developments" of the past three years had slowed down the realization of the functional program of the City of Hope, they had also quickened the human pulse. More people gave from the heart than from the purse, and we were justified in believing that our greatest asset was not recorded in a ledger or bankbook. Rather, it was inscribed in the hearts of the men, women, and children throughout the nation who made up our People's Movement—the "people" who were the lifeline of our City of Hope Medical Center.

16

Diagnosis—Cancer

IN ACCORDANCE with a long established precedent, the biennial City of Hope conventions were held in midsummer. But since the delegates came from all parts of the nation, there had been some agitation for changing the conventions to midwinter so that many of the visitors could escape the wintry blasts in their home areas and enjoy the perennial California sunshine.

The "unforeseen developments" which had slowed down the implementation of the mandates given us by the 1946 Convention made it expedient for us to yield, at that time, to the existing sentiment for holding the conventions in midwinter. The postponement gave us six more months within which to advance the program.

But then another "unforeseen development" occurred. When the delegates gathered in Los Angeles for the January 1949 convention, they witnessed an amazing phenomenon—the first snowstorm in the history of Southern California!

During the inspection tour of the City of Hope, which was a regular feature of the program, they all but froze and it was through falling snowflakes that they saw first evidence of the progress made toward the realization of their Medical Center. In the twenty-nine-month interval between the conventions, we had managed to complete, equip, and occupy the greater part of the new Central Medical Building, the bed capacity for tuberculous patients had been increased, and additional facilities made available for the more effective treatment and study of chest diseases.

Under the circumstances, fulfillment of the first mandate given us by the 1946 Convention was a noteworthy achievement. But it still remained to be seen whether a nationwide amalgam of people could build and support a philanthropic institution whose services extended beyond the limits of "bed capacity" and the immediate care of the sick.

We were blazing a new trail in trying to create a Medical Center which was to be administered and supported by thousands of people in all walks of life, the majority of them physically distant from Duarte. There was no precedent by which we could measure our chances for success. Similar undertakings were supported either by federal, state, or municipal taxes, through affiliation with large universities, or by invested capital.

In behalf of their constituents, the delegates to the 1949 Convention reaffirmed their determination to follow through with the Medical Center program as it had been enunciated by the 1946 Assembly. Basically, the second phase in our total program called for the establishment of facilities for the diagnosis and treatment of major diseases other than tuberculosis. The convention authorized the building of a one-hundred-bed hospital unit within the next two years, plus the necessary adjuncts for a related research and teaching program. Among other things, after a taste of California snow, the delegates also voted to restore midsummer as the season for future conventions!

The next step was to determine which of the so-called catastrophic diseases was to be our next adversary. A circumstance, common to the death of many people whose lives had been cut short by cancer, had been agitating my thoughts for a long time. It seemed to me that the universal lament was, "Too late." Time and again, I heard family members bemoaning the fact that the malignancy had been discovered "too late" for the medical intervention which might have prolonged or saved the lives of their loved ones.

I was the first to admit that cancer was a treacherous foe, attacking its victims from ambush, but the complacency about those fatal delays in discovering its presence was disquieting, nevertheless. I wondered whether delay was inevitable, because of the insidious nature of the disease, or whether it was more often the result of circumstances which could have been avoided.

History began to repeat itself as I sought the answers. Taking the only course open to a layman, I combed through medical histories hoping to gain an insight into the relationship between delay and recovery, discussed the problems with our medical staff, visited institutions devoted to the treatment of cancer patients, asked questions. I also requested our Medical Advisory Board to analyze, interpret, and define the facilities and personnel necessary to the inauguration of a concentrated fight against malignancies in the diagnostic clinic, hospitals, and laboratories.

Much to my surprise, the case histories I traced through medical reports revealed that cancer was not as deadly as its reputation had it. There was ample evidence that many types of malignancies could be, and had been, cured when diagnosed in their early stages. The more information I gathered about the nature of the disease, the more convinced I became that until diagnostic and therapeutic procedures used to combat cancer became more clearly defined, specialized management was vital to a cure.

I found that responsibility for the needlessly high cancer mortality rate had to be charged, alike, to the lay public and the medical profession. Ignoring symptoms of cancer was not always fatal but in the large majority of cases it was. Paradoxically enough, therefore, I found that the first cause for delay in seeing a doctor was the *fear* that he might find cancer. That deterrent could be alleviated, I felt, by debunking the widespread belief that all types of cancer were inevitably fatal.

When I arrived at the JCRA, in 1926, a definite diagnosis of tuberculosis had also been tantamount to a death sentence. Fear caused many people to ignore early evidences of the disease because they were not convinced that it was curable, even when diagnosed in its early stages. The same held true with cancer.

A second, and probably the most urgent, consideration in the delay of investigating cancer symptoms was the steep cost of a thorough examination. Another factor was the social stigma accompanying the disease, an outgrowth of the "hush-hush" attitude prevalent when little was known about its nature and, finally, the choice of a time convenient to business, work, or household responsibilities.

Comparing the experiences of people who, in various stages of the disease, had visited a doctor's office for confirmation or denial of their suspicions, I came to the conclusion that the large majority of general practitioners and surgeons were not capable of diagnosing or managing cancer cases effectively. Typically, when a patient entered a doctor's office, he took his place among many others who were waiting. If the doctor meant to see the ever-increasing patient load during designated office hours, while also taking telephone calls, it was humanly impossible for him to give more than cursory attention to each.

If the symptoms of the patient with suspected cancer happened to be fairly obvious, the doctor may have proceeded in the right direction. It seemed to me that any general medical practitioner worthy of his degree would recommend such cases to a specialized cancer clinic and hospital for a thorough diagnostic checkup and specialized management. Certainly it was more to his credit to err on the side of caution than to suggest, if symptoms were obscure, that "we keep a close watch on it." In the meantime, the patient's chances for life were left hanging in the balance.

A statement released by a leading cancer research foundation had revealed that with the procedures then known for the diagnosis and treatment of cancer, only one out of a possible three cures was being achieved. That posed the question, "Why weren't the other two cancer victims saved?" In the light of my survey, the obvious answer was that facilities for diagnosis and treatment had not been available to the "other two" for one reason or another. The logical solution, it seemed to me, would be to create specialized cancer hospitals throughout the United States, even as specialized sanatoria to combat tuberculosis had appeared on the national scene a quarter of a century before.

The treatment of cancer had gained momentum on various fronts. Surgical procedures were improving, the splitting of the atom had widened horizons in radiotherapy by producing radioactive isotopes, and chemotherapy was also being used to good advantage in the treatment of some types of cancer. I was convinced, therefore, that if all the known procedures for the diagnosis and treatment of cancer were to be brought together in specialized centers where they would be administered by cancer specialists, a far greater percentage of potential cures would be realized.

Based on my findings and the recommendations of our Medical Advisory Board, I suggested to the Board of Directors that we, the people of the City of Hope, enter the fight against cancer by establishing a Tumor and Allied Diseases Hospital and Out-patient Clinic which would make specialized diagnosis, treatment, and aftercare available to the

people on the same free basis which had been our
policy since the institution was founded. I realized
that it would be a major and costly undertaking but,
as ever, I was confident that our People's Movement
would provide the wherewithal for financing the necessary housing and purchase of vital equipment.

A tragic circumstance in our own family of City
of Hope supporters stimulated our determination to
inaugurate the first free, specialized cancer hospital
and diagnostic clinic under Jewish auspices in the
United States. A precocious twelve-year-old boy
who had been instrumental in organizing the first
City of Hope Youth Auxiliary in Los Angeles, and
was its president—a youngster whose talks before
university students, adult auxiliaries, and the 1949
Convention had inspired the founding of other youth
groups throughout the country—was stricken by
cancer and died when he was only fourteen years
old. We resolved that our Medical Center would be
in the vanguard of the fight against a merciless killer,
which strikes young and old indiscriminately, and
pinpointed 1950 as the year in which to make an
all-out effort to restore the momentum we had lost
during the previous years. Come what might, my
goal was the dedication of our cancer hospital and
clinic at the next Convention, which had been scheduled for June, 1951.

As always, our only collateral for progressive

growth between conventions was the anticipated contributions of our auxiliaries and other supporting groups and individuals who made up our People's Movement. In order to assure support commensurate with our increased needs it was necessary to bring our program to the attention of an ever-widening circle of people, and I took to the road again.

Toward the end of 1950, I began to feel run down and tired. It was not the first time, of course, that the hectic pace of traveling the country, and the tensions of building and maintaining a multi-million-dollar institution on an unorthodox financial basis had affected my usually robust health. After several superficial examinations I was assured there was nothing radically wrong, so I kept going until I was confident that our cancer hospital and clinic would be completed and ready for dedication at the 1951 Convention.

I still had reason to be concerned about the state of my health, however, and in February, 1951, I entered a general hospital for a physical checkup. A few days after admission I was informed that immediate surgery was indicated. Diagnosis—cancer!

17

Dedication

I COULD NOT BELIEVE, at first, that I had fallen victim to the very disease we had chosen to attack and I was in no mood to appreciate the irony of the situation. I could not ignore the awful truth that, abetted by my doctors, I had broken almost every one of our commandments against putting off early and specialized investigation of cancer symptoms. Based on my own convictions, I was forced to acknowledge that in all probability my days on this earth were numbered.

I had lived closely with death for many years and had often heard others, young and old, jest about its inevitability as long as the event was a vague probability of the future. But when the eventuality became imminent, there was only despair. Fortunately, nature comes to man's assistance and, in some measure, blocks out the ever-present awareness.

The City of Hope

I began to think about the many things that I must do before I underwent surgery, both for my personal affairs and for the Medical Center which was only then beginning to take real form. I wondered whether I would be around for the dedication of the Cancer Hospital.

I began to dictate many letters and a long series of instructions to my family and to the City of Hope administrative staff, promising them, one and all, that I would return to haunt them if they failed to guard and preserve the ideals, philosophy, and service for which I had worked so hard and dreamed so long. None of the material was of sufficient substance to satisfy me and I rued the fact that I had never taken time, really, to crystallize and record the ideology, philosophy, and functional patterns I hoped would be perpetuated at the City of Hope.

As scheduled, I underwent surgery on the morning of February 27, 1951, and shortly after the operation was assured that it had not been "too late" and that I could look forward to a cure. I began to discover for myself the value of the false hope I had so often dispensed during my early days at the sanatorium. When anyone, even the woman who mopped the floor of my hospital room every day, would say, "You're going to be all right," it gave me a tremendous lift, just because I wanted to believe it.

I began to consider the relative merits of telling,

or not telling, a patient stricken by cancer or any other major disease that death was imminent—that it was a matter of weeks, months, or even a year or more. There might possibly be circumstances which would make such a revelation necessary but, by and large, I was convinced that nothing was gained, and much lost, by depriving a patient of hope. Despite the bravado he might display for the public, his remaining days on earth would be clouded in despair.

Another consideration was that tomorrow something might turn up in a laboratory test tube to make these false hopes real. Probably the most dramatic example of that was the discovery of insulin for diabetics. I never failed to be moved by the story of Dr. Banting, walking down the long porch of his sanatorium and calling out happily to the diabetic patients who were waiting there for death: "I think I've got something for you!" Within a matter of hours after the first shots of insulin were administered to those "dying" people, they began to gain strength, and most of them were soon leading normal lives again.

Though I had been told that my chances for a cure were good, the course of my illness did not warrant optimism and I had become more or less resigned to the thought of an early separation from my family, friends, the City of Hope, and the world.

Recuperating from surgery at home, I devoted my time to writing more detailed "Testaments" to the

Board of Directors, the doctors, and other members of the City of Hope staff, offering suggestions for carrying on their work. My family was instructed to mail them when and if I departed this life. I also intensified my reading on cancer management in order to familiarize myself with the problems unique to the operation of a specialized cancer hospital and clinic.

The 1951 Convention was scheduled for the first week in July, and counting on regaining my strength in the intervening months, I began to work on my reports to the people. Then, three weeks after my return home from the hospital, I was stunned by the undeniable evidence that the cancer had not been entirely routed out, as I had been led to believe. On April 16, I was back on the operating table.

The physical and spiritual aftermath of those two major surgical ordeals in such close succession was bad enough. But the psychological shock of discovering that the malignancy had not been checked was far worse. I was convinced that my doctors, family, and friends had known all along that the surgery was "too late," and had only encouraged me to believe that I might anticipate a cure to spare my feelings. There was no doubt in my mind any more that I was due for an early exit from life and I resigned myself to that fate.

I then had first-hand knowledge of what it meant

110

to be stricken by a disease for which there was no definitive remedy after the early stages, and I planned to devote the time I had left to the implementation of a highly specialized cancer program at our Medical Center.

Back home once again, I completed my reports to the Convention and, under the impression that I would not live to see them realized, drew up proposals for the coming two years.

During the years I had traveled about the country, I had made personal friends of the people whose interest and support I had enlisted for the City of Hope and they made up a large majority of the delegates who attended the 1951 Convention. It was good to be back among my friends and co-workers once again and to share their pride in our accomplishments. Yet, under the circumstances, the Convention was an emotional as well as a physical strain. It was little more than two months after the second probing of my interior and I had not managed to regain my former vigor and aplomb.

The Tumor and Allied Diseases Hospital was dedicated on July 2nd. Among the more than fifteen hundred people who had gathered from near and far to witness and participate in the ceremonies were many noted civic, scientific, and philanthropic leaders.

The first speaker to be introduced by the president of our Board of Directors was the then Lieutenant-

Governor of the State of California. In paying high tribute to the people of the City of Hope, he pointed out that their humanitarianism and good will were practical demonstrations of the words spoken many centuries before by the Hebrew prophet, Micah:

> And what doth thy God require of thee except that ye love mercy, that ye judge wisely, and that ye walk humbly with thy God.

The merit of our specialized approach against major diseases was remarked by an official of the federal government long in the vanguard of the fight against cancer. He said:

> This hospital offers renewed hope not only to the cancer patient but also to the cancer scientist, the clinician, and the general public. The cancer patient can look to it as a place where he will receive the finest and most up-to-date medical care without regard to his financial status. All of us can look to it as an example of what can and must be done in other parts of the country to lessen the burden of the cancer patient. The research and clinical specialists can look to it as offering a unique opportunity to bring together their accumulated knowledge and experience. *For, in cancer especially, it is essential that research and clinical work be closely coordinated.*

A director of charities on the local scene paid tribute to our People's Movement:

> Yours is the only organization that has been able to raise enough money, privately, to build and carry on

a job of this kind, without help from other public or private agencies.

Still another leader on the Cancer front emphasized the therapeutic value of hope:

> The weakness in a cancer program is the inability of people to find a place where there is hope. Here, there is hope. You not only have a City of Hope where large numbers of people have found new hope, but you have become a symbol of hope to the whole United States.

A representative of a national welfare organization used me as an example of the spirit and dedication of the people of the City of Hope:

> Some human beings become fanatic about getting things done and Sam Golter is one of these. I have seen him in action . . . and I know the joy he must feel in witnessing this tremendous achievement.

"Joy," yes, but more important was justification of my belief that a great institution could be built and supported by a People's Movement.

Recognition of our efforts was the finest tonic I had yet received, and it restored my will to re-enter the fight against major diseases, concentrating on cancer, against which I now had a personal grudge.

When the president of the City of Hope had acknowledged all the gratifying tributes which were paid to our achievements and our goals, he called on me to cut the ribbon which would signal the official opening of our cancer hospital. It was a great moment for all our people of the City of Hope. And yet, because of my illness, the occasion was charged with sadness for me, my family, my co-workers, and my host of friends who had, for so long, shared my hopes and dreams. I could not control the lump in my throat when the president said:

> . . . to many of us, this great moment has deep significance but only to one man here does it represent the fulfillment of a dream. His vision, his determination in the face of all obstacles, and his indomitable courage, have made this moment possible.

Cutting the ribbon was my last official act for many months to come. The Convention had wisely resolved to devote full attention, during the next two years, to the development and consolidation of our new, specialized medical facilities. I, in turn, retired to lick my wounds.

18

We Believe . . .

ON THE CHANCE that I was making my final appearance before the group which represented every facet of our People's Movement, I had presented a "credo" of sorts in my report to the Convention. But during my enforced leisure I began to wonder how I could preserve the basic philosophy and values, inherent in our City of Hope program, for those who followed in our footsteps. I wanted to be sure the spiritual values would never become secondary to the physical development and that the City of Hope would stand, through the years, as an example of man's humanity to man.

Weeks stretched into months and the course I had been expecting my illness to take did not materialize. In fact just the reverse happened. I began to gain weight, get stronger, and develop a better spirit. With the renewal of hope that I might, after all, have an extended lease on life, I set about in earnest to embody our credo in a letter addressed to the "Friends of the City of Hope."

In a foreword, I acknowledged that "there comes a time when we must recognize the mortality of human beings and the immortality of ideas and ideals." Since my own future had become uncertain, I wanted to perpetuate ". . . the set of principles which had evolved at the City of Hope during the four decades of its existence. They are unique in character and in concept."

In recording the City of Hope Credo, I had emulated the noted physician and philosopher, Maimonides, by embodying our principles in "Thirteen Articles of Faith." ". . . and like him, we, the people of the City of Hope, also *believe with a wholehearted faith.*"

A Doorway to Hope

WE BELIEVE . . .
Since the span of human life is short compared to the long
    procession of time, and
Since disease constantly threatens and often succeeds in
    terminating life before the normal course is run,
It is incumbent upon us to rescue those who are physically
    shipwrecked and help them round out their full span
    of years.

—Article I

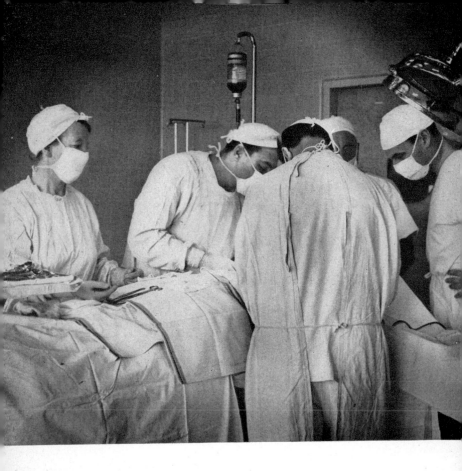

Specialized Surgical Procedures

WE BELIEVE . . .

Since major diseases are often difficult to diagnose and costly
to treat, and

Since specialized diagnosis and management are the most
effective weapons against certain major diseases,

It is our duty to provide specialized medical and surgical
services for needy victims of such diseases.

—Article II

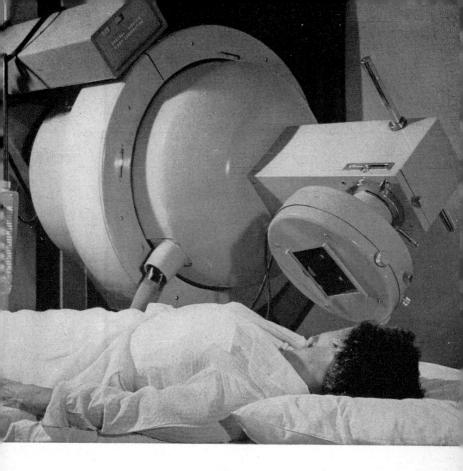

The Maxitron—One of the Specialized Weapons Used in the Fight against Cancer

WE BELIEVE . . .

Since recovery often depends on confidence in the care received, and

Since specialized diagnosis and treatment of major illnesses can be carried on more effectively in a professionally staffed and scientifically equipped medical center,

It is our duty to create such a center where work is performed by a full-time staff of dedicated doctors, technicians, and nurses, unhampered by outside interests, and augmented by specialists in private practice who are willing and able to contribute their services.

—Article III

Fighting Disease in the Laboratory

WE BELIEVE . . .

Since the fight against major diseases must be waged in the research laboratory as well as in the clinic, the hospital, and the conference room, and

Since a medical center which embodies specialized hospitals, clinics, and laboratories offers unique opportunities for medical education,

It is our duty to create facilities for basic and clinical research and medical education.

—Article IV

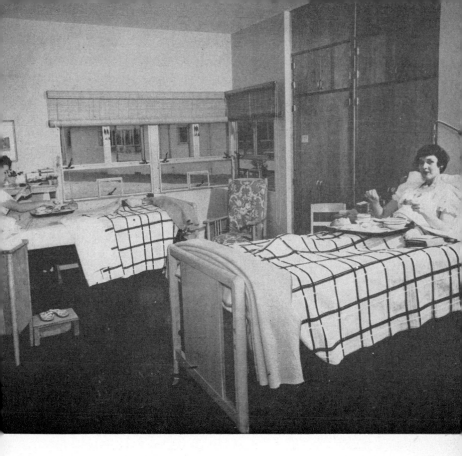

There Are No Wards.

WE BELIEVE . . .

Since the fight against major diseases requires maximum
  physical and mental strength, and

Since financing the effective treatment of a major disease is
  beyond the reach of many people,

It is our duty to give all necessary care and treatment on a
  free basis in order to assure the peace of mind which
  is so vital to ultimate recovery.

—Article V

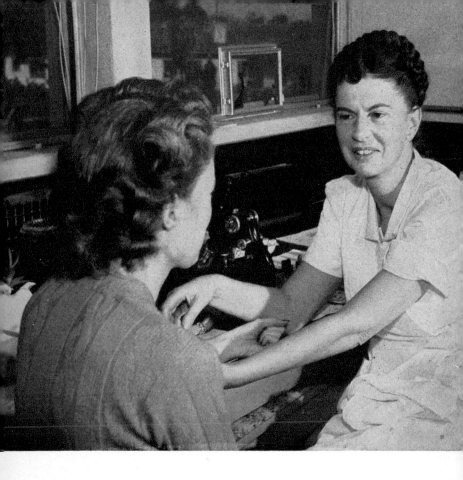

Free Service—with Dignity

We Believe . . .

Since a high spirit is vital in the fight against disease, and

Since the sense of being a recipient of charity lowers morale, and

Since there is no profit in saving the body if, in the process, we destroy the soul,

It is our duty to maintain the dignity and self-respect of the patient by avoiding the implication of charity in our service.

—Article VI

Preservation of the Family Unit

We Believe . . .

Since the home is the foundation of our civilization and the source of our happiness, and

Since the cost of treating a major disease tends to pauperize the family and threatens the security of the home,

It is our duty to assume the financial responsibility and thereby help to maintain the dignity of the family and the unity of the home.

—Article VII

Friendly Interviews

WE BELIEVE . . .

Since victims of major diseases tend to recover more rapidly
under gentle, kind and considerate care, and

Since people who have a personal, rather than an impersonal,
attitude can more effectively render such care,

It is our duty to bring into our service only those who are
motivated by a deep, humanitarian impulse.

—Article VIII

The Atmosphere Is Serene.

We Believe . . .
Since we do not always succeed in our fight to save life, and
Since it may be necessary to attend a patient as life wanes,
It is our duty under such circumstances to create an atmos-
     phere of kindness, love, and compassion.

—Article IX

The Sense of Personal Participation

We Believe . . .
Since the restoration of health and the saving of human life
is the responsibility of all mankind, and
Since our unique service requires the voluntary participation
of a nationwide community of people in all walks of life,
It is right that the work of the City of Hope should be supported by a People's Movement.

—Article X

We do not ask of an unfortunate, "What country do you come from?" or "What is your religion?"

We Believe . . .

Since every human being has the right to life, health, and opportunity, regardless of race, creed or nationality, and

Since the sick should not be denied medical care because of race, creed, or nationality, and

Since the individual should not be discriminated against because of race, creed, or nationality,

It is our duty to practice a broad nonsectarian policy in all our services, in accordance with the American principle of democracy.

—Article XI

A New Source of Spiritual Nourishment

WE BELIEVE . . .

Since "Man does not live by bread alone," and

Since values which constitute an enriched spiritual diet have been created and nurtured by the people of the City of Hope, and

Since helping our less fortunate fellow man offers sustenance for the spirit,

It is true that personal participation in the People's Movement of the City of Hope is a source of spiritual nourishment.

—Article XII

New Apostles

We Believe . . .

Since materialism is rampant in our society, and

Since the antidote for materialism is a return to spiritual, moral, and ethical values, and

Since the City of Hope is fostering these values,

It is incumbent upon us to bring our philosophies, our aims, and objectives to the attention of the people of our nation.

—Article XIII

The Arsenal (Chapter 20)

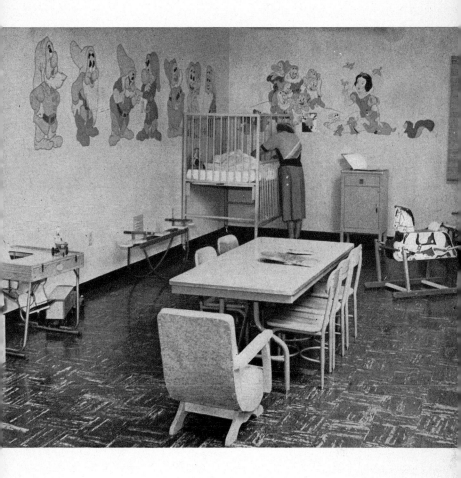

Parent Participation—Leukemia Wing (Chapter 22)

The Ever Vigilant Nurse (Chapter 24)

19

The Cancer Cell

THOSE WHO BELIEVE that an ill wind must inevitably blow somebody good will probably make a case out of the fact that I was stricken by cancer. It is true that when I returned to full harness, on January 1, 1952, I was more determined than ever to spur a fight against the disease. In addition, others whose lives had been affected by cancer, either directly or indirectly, began to demonstrate a feeling of closer kinship with me.

Judging from the endless tales of woe poured into my sympathetic ear, few people had escaped the cancer blight and each of them had a story to tell. These personal case histories, weighed against the information I had gathered from almost incessant reading on the subject during my long convalescence, furnished a plentiful supply of grist for my mental mill. I became convinced, beyond the shadow of a doubt, that early diagnosis and specialized management were the only hopes for reducing the excessively high rate of cancer mortality.

Paradoxically enough, however, I also believed that specialization necessarily tended to narrow the horizons of those who apply themselves, assiduously, to a specific problem and that an informed layman might therefore be better qualified to make an appraisal leading to a realization of the total objective. An outstanding example of this was the work of Colonel, later General, Groves, who was a layman in the field of science. It was his capable mobilization of human and physical resources that expedited a successful search for the catalyst which was necessary to the production of the atom bomb.

There was no serious lack of activity in the field of cancer research at that time but it was all widely scattered and loosely coordinated. Based on my studies and observations, I felt sure that a solution for the cancer problem could also be expedited if a campaign were as efficiently integrated under a single head, preferably a layman, who would have the same unlimited funds at his disposal.

Furthermore, I believed it was time for the lay public to stop looking on the fight against disease as a Sacred Cow, to be kept within the exclusive province and prerogative of the medical profession. Ignorance about any disease only heightens fear,

118

reduces the sense of individual responsibility, and loses sight of the important part played by the body in fighting off enemy invaders.

Long before the advent of the medicine man, nature—in its drive to perpetuate the species—created effective defense mechanisms in the human body which go into spontaneous action against almost every alien infiltration. Specialized units of red and white corpuscles, and other antibodies, declare war on the enemy and, by the time the doctor arrives, are already counterattacking. Those natural defenses, reinforced by other troops as yet unidentified—the Secret Service, as it were—bear the brunt of the fight against the invader. The noise of that combat, heard through a stethoscope, and the heat of battle registered on a thermometer, help the doctor locate and identify the enemy.

It is not my intent to minimize the vital aid given the body by the doctor, but if there were a yardstick for measuring comparative contributions to the successful outcome of the fight against most diseases, I believe the body would be given the lion's share of the credit.

In the fight against cancer, however, the ratio is reversed and the doctor bears almost total responsibility for conducting a successful campaign. For some reason not yet understood, the body does not mobilize its defenses for an attack against the tumor cell and it is the very lack of that cooperation which makes cancer so difficult to locate and identify. Some scientists claim that the body does resent intrusion of the tumor cell and puts up a form of token resistance. The fact has never been clearly established, however, and there is more reason to believe that the body gives aid and comfort to the enemy, providing housing, nourishment, and a climate exactly to its liking.

Just a superficial knowledge of the action of tumor cells in the human body serves to emphasize the urgency of an immediate investigation should their presence be suspected. As a general rule, the various organs of the body adhere to the rules and regulations of a systematic physical order. As long as the cell, which is the smallest bodily unit, hews to the line and follows directives from a central headquarters, it is essential to the continuance of life. But just as the offspring of model citizens in our human society often become delinquent, so the offspring of law-abiding cells may fail to conform to established standards of behavior. They refuse to obey orders, go on a rampage and, from the unseemly rate at which they propagate, would seem to indulge, intemperately, in sexual orgies. Whatever the compulsion, the fact remains that tumor cells reproduce themselves at a rate and in a manner contrary to all laws of normal cell behavior. In turn, the ever-increasing colony of rebel cells gluts itself at the expense of its neighbors who weaken and die for lack of life-sustaining nourishment.

In more ways than one, the tumor cell follows the pattern of another insidious development in our human society—the Communist "cell." The Right Wingers follow a benign course and while their rapid reproduction crowds and inconveniences the normal cells in their vicinity, they do not destroy them.

The Leftists are the real troublemakers. They adopt a militant, or malignant, course. Not content to destroy the tissue in which they originally set up activities, they also invade neighboring tissue for destructive purposes. Even worse, they send their offspring to other parts of the body on errands of mischief and seem to have a canny knack for finding the most vulnerable spots for their attack. In this activity, too, some organs of the body act as a Fifth Column, cooperating with the enemy by providing unrestricted travel via blood vessels, arteries, and lymph glands.

If symptoms are investigated and the malignancy diagnosed while the tumor cells are still localized, they can be attacked more effectively. But once they have left their headquarters on errands of sabotage in other parts of the body, it is an almost impossible task, even for trained medical sleuths, to track them down. There is a definite dateline beyond which the doctor's intervention can be of little help in halting the subversive action of malignant tumor cells. As that dateline approaches, the margin of hope narrows. The difference between a possible cure and death, therefore, may very well be the one day, or even one hour, an individual puts off a visit to the doctor.

Whether there is promise of high or low hope, therefore, depends on the action taken by the patient and the doctor before that mythical dateline. Certainly, it is tragic enough when hope vanishes for unavoidable reasons but the tragedy is far greater when hope is lost through negligence!

That is why I believe that patients with even a suggestion of cancer should be given the benefit of a diagnostic workup in a medical center where personnel and facilities are dedicated exclusively to a fight against the disease. It is only logical that the trained eye of a cancer radiologist can best interpret X-rays of the area where the disease may be lurking. Similarly, the experienced cancer pathologist can best differentiate among normal, benign, and malignant cells and, from their appearance, recognize the specific section of the body from which they came. Even then, the margin for error is considerable. Should there be a definite diagnosis of cancer, immediate management of the case by cancer specialists can be considered the *only* correct procedure.

No one would expect a TV technician to treat an

ailing car motor as effectively as one who has a specialized knowledge of its inner workings and long experience in tracking down its unique quirks. By the same token, we cannot expect a general practitioner or surgeon who may see two or three cases of cancer in a year to be as capable of diagnosing and treating the disease as those whose every thought and effort are concentrated on its study and management.

The City of Hope is blazing a trail in the direction of creating a highly specialized medical center under philanthropic auspices for fighting cancer and other major diseases. Functionally, our services are provided free of all cost in order to make our facilities available to those stricken by the diseases which are treated and studied in our hospitals.

Our forte is specialization in every phase of the fight against the diseases treated in our Medical Center. Our doctors, surgeons, scientists, radiologists, pathologists, technicians, nurses, social workers, and heads of ancillary services—all work in teams, each a specialist in his respective field, each bringing wide experience and specialized knowledge to bear on individual cases.

20

Cancer Research

THE IDEA of crusading against cancer quickened the interest of the people of the City of Hope, and some of our newer auxiliaries even called themselves "Cancer Fighters." The mobilization of professional cancer fighters, however, presented a really formidable problem. Cancer specialists who were willing to forego private practice for an institutional career were hard enough to find, and the field narrowed down considerably with the specification that they must also subscribe to and practice the humanitarian approach which is an integral part of City of Hope ideology.

The need to minister to the soul while curing the body looms even larger in the treatment of cancer than it did in the early days of the JCRA. There was always the hope, then, that nature might effect a spontaneous cure of tuberculosis, but the doctor is the only hope of the cancer patient.

As our cancer program developed and I observed the steady stream of patients referred to our diagnostic clinic and cancer hospital by their doctors, I decided that giving free hospital and medical care was not enough. We could not hope to accommodate all the desperate people who turned to us for help and it was obvious that a better approach to the cancer problem was yet to be found. Research was the answer.

Unlike delinquent children who can be reformed, once a cell has taken a malignant course it cannot be restored to a normal status. In my opinion, therefore, the only perfect solution would be the development of a preventive. I believe it is within reason to expect that an antibiotic will eventually be found that can produce a bodily environment which, deadly for the rebel cells, will not affect the normal cells adversely. That is a layman's opinion, of course, but it does not stem from wishful thinking alone. It is based on the fact that since the behavior of the tumor cell differs so radically from that of the normal cell, there must also be a variance in their vulnerability. It remains, therefore, to discover that "Achilles' Heel" through research.

Fired by the idea of stimulating a search for a cure or preventive, I began to think and talk "research," giving little thought to practical considerations. I was interested only in finding a cure for cancer, and, with the pioneers of the City of Hope, I believed that "If the cause is right, the money will come from somewhere." From almost every other quarter and, oddly enough, from members of the professional staff in particular, the first reaction was: "Have you got the funds for it?"

I began to probe every avenue which might lead to an intensified cancer research program at the City of Hope and finally came on one which did not lead to a dead end. The School of Medicine of the University of California at Los Angeles agreed to transfer certain of its research teams to the City of Hope and we, in turn, were to finance the program, devoted exclusively to a search for causes and cures of the specific diseases treated in our Medical Center. It was an ambitious project for us to undertake. In addition to meeting the considerable payroll for a large staff of research scientists, we had to provide costly equipment and elaborate facilities for its housing. But when the Medical Research Institute of the City of Hope was dedicated on July 18, 1952, we had taken one more step toward the building of a stronghold from which we could concentrate an attack against man's worst enemy—disease.

During the course of the investigations and observations which led to our research affiliation with

UCLA, I discovered that many of the shortcomings which exist in the medical field also apply to research. Mismanagement of cancer cases by certain elements of the medical profession could be charged to apathy or negligence. In research, lack of initiative, too little resourcefulness, and timidity are the culprits. In this effort, too, overconservatism tends to hamper and slow down progress. The trait, admirable under some circumstances, cannot be justified, however, when the legal tender is human life. A too close adherence to pedagogic procedures by the scientist inhibits the unorthodox approaches which may have merit. Furthermore, the slow, methodical, tried-and-true processes contribute to the widespread lethargy which, under normal conditions, is characteristic of the scientific world.

It has been seen, however, that the scientist can be spurred into radical and aggressive action when roused by a sense of urgency. I do not believe it is mere coincidence that some of the greatest medical, scientific and technological developments of the twentieth century are the constructive by-products of a war effort. Fighting a war stimulates the scientific world into action and the achievement of any end necessary to the nation's successful conduct of that war transcends the expenditure of money and even human life. It seems illogical to me, therefore, that so many of those who voluntarily dedicate their lives to the war against disease (which takes a far greater toll of life than military war) are denied the dollars with which to carry on the fight. Yet the conquest of cancer alone would do more to make the world a better and safer place to live for all peoples, than all the wars which have ever been fought! I venture to say that if a cure for cancer became necessary for the political aggrandizement of any nation, it would not be long before a solution to the problem were found.

The fear that government appropriations earmarked for medical research may be misapplied seems to have a paralyzing effect on those who hold the purse strings, and the legitimate investigators suffer right along with the illegitimate. The few dollars that may be saved by such over-conscientious concern in allocating research grants cannot begin to offset the danger of losing a great opportunity. Scientists who are faced with worry over the availability of funds with which to carry on their work cannot concentrate their total energies on the problem at hand.

In discussing the problems of building up a research program with technicians of many prominent laboratories, as well as individual investigators, the consensus seems to be that, too often, the criterion for the allocation of research funds is the number of square feet of gleaming white tile and highly polished chromium equipment. That may account for the fact that so many discoveries which have proved a boon to mankind have come out of dingy, make-shift laboratories manned by dedicated investigators who had the courage to pursue an imaginative theory. At the City of Hope, we are concentrating on bringing into our service not only the most able scientists we can find, but those with daring and imagination as well—characteristics which are vital to venturesome raids against the diseases treated and studied in our Medical Center.

The lay people must also rouse themselves to the urgent need for medical research and appreciate what it can mean to their ultimate welfare. Our People's Movement is keyed to that trend. We have proved that the "man in the street" is interested in the fight to prolong and save human life and that, given the opportunity, he will participate in the fight.

21

Apostles

FROM the very inception of the idea for a medical center, I realized that it could be brought into being only through the exceptional efforts of devoted and inspired people, and that their fervor and enthusiasm for the program could be transmitted to others only by word of mouth. The 1958 Convention was therefore geared to the indoctrination of the delegates and the keynote for that assembly was "Apostles."

It had taken six years to convert the sanatorium into a specialized medical center and most of the delegates were seeing it in full operation for the first time. They were excited and pleased about the modern structures, the highly specialized equipment and facilities, and the extent of the life-saving services which their efforts and sacrifices had made possible. I was anxious to impress on them, however, that these were physical manifestations which could have been created by many others equally as well, and that if we were to succeed in blazing a trail toward the building of a better human society, it was vital that we point out the unique philosophy of the City of Hope in translating our program to the people of the nation.

Mulling over ways to present our total program simply and effectively, I decided to base my report to the delegates on a pronouncement which had prefaced each day's session of religious instruction during my boyhood in Russia. With a rigid finger pointed in my direction, the teacher would startle me out of the reveries to which I have always been prone by booming out: "On three things the world stands: *Law, Worship, Benevolence!*" Then, depending on his mood, he would devote the lesson to one of the three "things." I often wonder if he realized how ably he had succeeded in inculcating that fundamental lesson into one of his apparently inattentive pupils.

My report was cast on a paraphrase of that profound declaration. "On three pillars the City of Hope stands: *Service, Humanitarianism, Reward.*"

The first pillar—*Service*—represents our functional program and supports the arsenal from which we launch our attack against the diseases which take the greatest toll of human life.

In our *hospitals,* we provide specialized medical,

surgical, and physical care for victims of those diseases.

In our *research laboratories,* we are engaged in a concentrated search for causes and cures of the specific diseases treated in our hospitals.

In our *outpatient clinics,* we provide specialized and thorough diagnostic services, to encourage the early investigation of symptoms suggesting the presence of any of the diseases we are fighting. Necessary after-care is also provided on an outpatient basis for patients discharged from the hospitals.

In our *lecture rooms,* we have provided facilities for instructing graduate medical students in the specialized procedures used and developed in our Medical Center for diagnosing and treating the diseases included in our service program.

An important adjunct to our hospitals is the Department of Social Welfare which is concerned with the well-being of the patients and their families, and, in keeping with our philosophy of treating the person as well as the disease, many vital ancillary departments and services have been integrated into our functional program.

The second pillar—*Humanitarianism*—supports the ideology and philosophy embodied in our Thirteen Articles of Faith, as they relate to *free service, preservation of human dignity,* and *nonsectarianism.*

The fight for life requires modern, specialized weapons which must be made available to those who lack the financial means to wage a costly campaign against major diseases. In order to remove worry and obstacles which may stand in the way of recovery, the City of Hope provides physical, medical, and surgical care for its patients on a completely free basis.

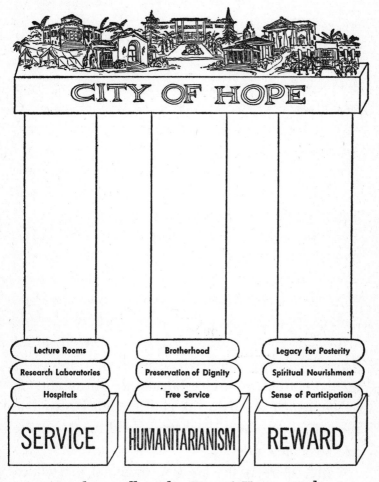

On three pillars the City of Hope stands.

Providing free service is not enough in itself. We believe "there is no profit in curing the body if, in the process, we destroy the soul," and we make every effort to preserve the dignity and self-respect of the patient and his family. We have excluded the word "charity" from our vocabulary and substituted the precept: "I am my brother's keeper."

Free service and preservation of human dignity are not enough if they are offered on a restrictive basis. They must apply alike to all people, regardless of race, creed, or nationality, because we, the people of the City of Hope, believe that every human being is entitled to a chance for life.

The third pillar is *Reward*. The City of Hope is a monument to the spirit, will, and energy of the dedicated workers who make up our People's Movement. In return for their efforts and sacrifices, their reward is threefold:

First, there is the joy which comes from a *sense of participation* in a movement which has as its goal the adding of "years to life and life to years."

Second, there is the rich *spiritual nourishment* which stems from an awareness that they are instrumental not only in saving human life but in creating values which can light the path for others to follow toward the building of a better world for themselves and their neighbors.

Third, there is the creation of moral and ethical

134

standards which constitute an *enduring legacy* for their posterity.

In closing my report, I pointed out that: "The City of Hope is not only a house of healing, a center for medical research and education, a reservoir for the creation of spiritual and ethical values. It is a way of life—a *new* way of life which embraces the trends of tomorrow."

The effectiveness of the apostolic theme of our 1953 Convention was demonstrated almost immediately. Returning home on the train, one of the delegates struck up a conversation with a passenger who, as it turned out, was the editor of a widely distributed nurses' publication. That casual meeting between a newly indoctrinated apostle and her prospective convert resulted in the appearance of a feature article in the magazine which told the City of Hope story to thousands of people.

The circumstances of their meeting were told in the "Editor's Note":

> Both of us were returning eastward aboard the Golden Gate Limited. From her, I learned of the City of Hope—learned about it and loved it. Loved it because I know how great is the need all over the world for a City of Hope where brotherhood may be constantly proved.
>
> "We are dedicated to the work," the attractive, soft-voiced woman told me, "we work very hard but we adore it."

Wherever you are, wherever you live. . . . Remember—part of your hope is in the City of Hope!

On a tour around the nation in the fall of 1953, I saw a notable increase in the number of dedicated workers enlisted in our cause, and was encouraged by the evidence that our People's Movement had picked up the momentum which was so vital to the maintenance and growth of our Medical Center.

I began to appreciate even more keenly the wisdom and foresight of the early pioneers of the sanatorium in going ahead with their plans for the building of a desert oasis for tuberculous victims, without first seeking the backing of monied interests. They chose to rely on the interest and participation of many people whose hearts were touched by the plight of their fellow men—people who were unable to give large sums of money so gave themselves instead. Yes, they chose to mortgage their *efforts* in order to provide an urgently needed service. The fact that most of them lived in adversity themselves was reflected in their compassionate attitude toward human suffering and their humanitarian concepts relating to the preservation of the dignity of the patients who were the recipients of free service. There is a radical difference between free service provided by people who have a sympathetic and personal interest in one's welfare and the free service administered by the cold and disinterested hand of charity.

Apostles

The City of Hope came into being during an era when great fortunes could still be amassed without restraint of any kind. Some of that concentrated wealth found its way into charitable channels but while the dollars may have been many, the givers were few.

That was an era when people were more prone to receive than they are today. But even then the builders of the City of Hope held the dignity of man in such high regard that they did not relish the demeaning aspect and stigma of professional philanthropy. They anticipated the day when the "givers" would be one with the "receivers."

The City of Hope is not endowed, has no invested capital, or other more conventional sources of income. Auxiliaries, other supporting groups, and interested individuals are the lifeline of the Medical Center, and any monies received and designated for specific studies or services are supplementary. Unlike other programs which limit fund-raising activities to a given period each year, the City of Hope cannot exist on intermittent activities followed by long periods of inaction. We must seek funds all year round.

We have been criticized as aggressive by those who do not understand that constant awareness is vital to a People's Movement—that ours is a way of life which must be lived three hundred and sixty-five days a year—that personal participation in our humanitarian program nourishes the spirit and marks a return to those moral and ethical values which can make better people of us all—three hundred and sixty-five days a year!

22

Leukemia

I HAD BEEN especially pleased by the reaction of the Convention delegates to our entry into the fight against cancer because I knew their enthusiasm would be translated into support for the program. The cancer campaign covered so vast a sphere of action that there was danger of over-extending our "supply line." Yet the fact that the people of the City of Hope were eager for the fight encouraged me to broaden our attack.

As our staff of professional cancer fighters expanded, I saw an opportunity to establish a service which had been on my mind since 1950, following a trip to the various centers of our activities throughout the West. I had had no time for social visits, so at one port of call an acquaintance with whom I had worked during a charitable campaign some years before came to the airport to see me off. It was obvious that he was under severe stress and when we were having lunch he told me that his fifteen-year-old daughter had just died of leukemia.

When he related the incidents preceding the death of his child, I was so overwrought by the tragedy that I left the table abruptly and paced an anteroom until I was composed enough to return and face his terrible grief. The frantic but futile search the parents had made for something, or somebody, to save her life, and their pitiful efforts to keep the fact of her impending death from the child, haunt me to this day. Knowing that she would be with them only a matter of a few weeks, at most, they took her on a shopping tour and delighted the youngster by planning occasions at which she would wear the new dresses and accessories they had bought for her.

On the return flight, I could not get the thought of the child's death out of my mind. It seemed incredible to me that man, who could fly through space in heavier-than-air machines, had to stand by helplessly and watch innocent children die. Strange, too, that the same people who pay homage to the heroism of a man who, on the spur of the moment, gives his life to save another, the same people who condone the call for volunteers to risk almost certain death to gain a technical advantage on the battlefield, also criticize radical ventures in the field of medical experimentation. There are some among them who even object to the use of animals for that purpose. I wonder if any of them have ever experienced the terrible frustration of standing by the bedside of a dying child, trying desperately but hopelessly to keep the spark of life from going out.

By the time I got off the plane, I had made up my mind that just as soon as the opportunity presented itself, we, the people of the City of Hope, would take up arms against leukemia. The time seemed ripe following the 1953 Convention and, deciding to act first and worry about funds later, I began to search the field for someone to captain that fight. In September, 1953, we engaged an outstanding authority in the leukemic field and he brought with him his entire fighting team—men seasoned for that type of warfare. He was given full authority to inaugurate a specialized center for the care and treatment of leukemia victims and to develop a concentrated research program. Once more it was a case of: "If the cause is right, the money will come from somewhere."

In October of 1953, one of the major TV stations in Los Angeles, in cooperation with leading newspapers, enlisted the services of talent representing every phase of the entertainment world and held a seventeen-hour "telethon" to raise funds for our proposed children's cancer and leukemia hospital. The response to that appeal confirmed my confidence in the willingness of all people to participate in the fight

141

against disease. The heartwarming sentiments, expressed in notes and letters accompanying most of the contributions, indicated a particular determination to line up in the fight against those diseases which attack and kill little children.

On Decoration Day, 1954, the first two of the thirty-two cribs in our children's hospital were occupied. A little girl and a little boy came there, wide eyed and apprehensive of the strange environment, but feeling secure because someone familiar was standing by—their mothers. A unique feature of the Pediatric Hospital is the program for parent participation. Mothers and fathers are encouraged to share in the daily care of their children.

The wing is gay and colorful, designed as a playroom within a hospital. Each room bears the name of a cartoon character, beloved of children, which Walt Disney artists painted on the walls. An outdoor playground will give the children an opportunity to enjoy the normal play of childhood—as long as they are physically able to play.

Within a few months, most of the cribs and beds were occupied. The sight of those children and their frantic parents has become the bane of my life. Since, at present, we are unable to promise them anything more than that the lives of their children may be prolonged, my only crumb of comfort is the fact that I can say to the parents: "This is your hospital. Make yourselves at home and help yourselves to anything you need."

It is only when I think back to the days when our tuberculous patients, too, had to die, and realize that now we are able to save them, that I find hope for the future, knowing that a solution will be—must be— found for this tragic problem too.

The steady increase in our specialized staff of doctors and scientists has also made it possible for us to inaugurate a program of heart surgery for adults and children suffering from certain types of heart malfunctions. One of our surgeons, who was among the first to encourage and use surgery to relieve certain heart diseases, convinced me that the life-saving possibilities in that field are unlimited. While our fight against heart diseases is still in its infancy and only twenty beds are allocated for patients in that department, we are already rendering a major service in saving many people whose lives would otherwise be cut short.

Since early diagnosis is still the prime factor in the fight against all the diseases in which we specialize, we also saw an opportunity to utilize our constantly increasing professional staff to augment the free diagnostic services provided in our Outpatient Clinics. In an effort to avoid the "production line" atmosphere of many free clinics, many patients are seen only by appointment.

We are already examining many patients referred to us by physicians from throughout the nation and, on an ever-increasing basis, we are receiving packages containing X-rays, tissue specimens, and slides which have been mailed to us by doctors. Accompanying letters ask us to confirm or refute their original diagnoses. Confirmation of an early diagnosis of a malignancy is, of course, vitally important to the ultimate recovery of those unseen patients but it is of equal importance and far more gratifying to be able to report, in some instances, that the disease indicated by symptoms is not present.

While our facilities and staff are being expanded day by day, they lag far behind the demand for our services. Since we are unable to accommodate all who seek admission to our hospitals, we are forced to adhere, more and more rigidly, to the practice of selecting as in-patients only those whose lives, in the opinion of our medical staff, can be saved or prolonged as a result of the specialized care and treatment we are able to provide.

We, the people of the City of Hope, are proud of the role we are playing in the fight against major diseases. The unprecedented demand for our services indicates the urgent need for specialized medical centers under philanthropic auspices and if we have been instrumental in establishing a trend in that direction, all our trials and tribulations will have been justified. *Because the creation of such centers can stem only from the humanitarian impulse which promises a return to those moral and ethical values which separate man from beast.*

23

Professionals

WHEN WE REFER to "The people of the City of Hope," we visualize two branches of a family whose services in behalf of the Medical Center are interdependent. The volunteer workers who make up our People's Movement are the lifeline—the breadwinners as it were—and the professional staff "Keep the home fires burning." The two families live and work together harmoniously, their services are complementary, and each, in its own way, is vital to the operation of the City of Hope.

Our professional staff, too, is representative of people from all walks of life and all racial, religious, and ethnic groups. The many divisions of its service are also as numerous and as varied as the segments of society which make up our People's Movement.

By "professional," we mean salaried. The category includes doctors, nurses, technicians, office workers, social workers, cooks, dieticians, public relations and fund-raising personnel, ground keepers, and many, many others without whose services the City of Hope could not function. Just as it is necessary to indoctrinate our family of volunteers in the broader implications of our program and to develop apostles from its ranks, so it is of equal importance that each sector of our professional staff should know, believe, and reflect our unique ideology and philosophy. We must win apostles on that level also.

When I first came to America, I had seen the unhappy lot of the wage earner before the introduction of collective bargaining and I was fully aware of the value of the system for establishing equitable rates of compensation. In the early development of the City of Hope, therefore, I had encouraged the setting up of a collective bargaining agency for our people. As our program developed, however, I began to realize that collective bargaining standards for measuring the ratio between service and compensation were not entirely compatible with a humanitarian service dedicated to the saving and prolonging of human life.

The relentless diseases we are fighting attack around the clock, seven days a week, three hundred and sixty-five days a year. They have no respect for holidays—national or religious—and in order to counterattack their inroads effectively, we must be free to fight them on equal terms. The hours and efforts of our professional people, therefore, must be regulated by need, not by the timeclock. It has been a stroke of good fortune that the leaders of our union affiliation and of the Nurses' Association have recognized our singular problems and are today cooperating with us wholeheartedly in carrying out our humanitarian aims and objectives. As a result, our professional staff is as dedicated to the cause as our volunteers. The dollars they receive as compensation would never be adequate for the services they give. They, too, count their reward in terms of the personal and spiritual satisfaction they derive from participation in a humanitarian program, realizing that in the final analysis they are working not for the City of Hope but for their fellow man.

Working for compensation in a profit-making organization is one thing; working for compensation in a charitable organization is another; but working for the City of Hope is different from both. Our problems are as unique as our aims and objectives, and our approach to those problems is also singular and often unorthodox. Procedures which may be acceptable almost anywhere else in carrying out seemingly comparable services are not always effective in the implementation of our program. For example, our "fund raisers" are not primarily interested in getting dollars. Our philosophy calls for a conscious giving of self rather than a spontaneous gesture of giving, followed by a lack of interest in the application of the gift. For that reason, we often find it less difficult to train those who are novices in our various services than to "unlearn" and re-train those who have had extensive experience in other fields of endeavor.

That members of our professional staff have found "extra" compensation in working for the City of Hope is evidenced by the many people in our service who have devoted their lives to the cause and who count no obstacle sufficiently great to discourage them from carrying out a necessary program of work. I have heard them called "eager beavers." I call them "dedicated."

The hallmark of our professional workers, wherever they may be and in whatever capacity they may serve, is a devoted and dedicated application to the work of the City of Hope. Material compensation is not the sole measure of their efforts. If it were, they would not be working for the City of Hope.

24

Nurses

THE TWO CATEGORIES of our professional staff which are most immediately concerned with carrying out the services basic to our functional and ideological programs are, of course, the doctors and nurses.

Their part in our total program is to do everything possible, within the limits only of medical science, to save and prolong the lives of our patients and to spare no effort in maintaining the dignity of the suffering people who are the recipients of our free service.

It is vital that they, even more than any other component of our professional staff, ascribe to and practice the ideological principles expressed in our eighth Article of Faith, which states that, since gentle care and a personal attitude help a sufferer to recover more quickly, we must bring into our service only those motivated by a deep humanitarian impulse.

The very nature of the diseases treated in our hospitals makes that humanitarian impulse imperative. It is bad enough to be the victim of one of these diseases without having the additional problem of coping with hostile or indifferent attitudes on the part of those to whom the patient must look for hope.

Because the nurse is the immediate source of their physical well-being and comfort, and is in close contact with patients day and night, she has the greatest opportunity to maintain morale and self-respect. I, for one, am glad this is so. I believe the patient-nurse relationship can more nearly fulfill our humanitarian concepts than any other, and that the nursing profession merits the respect and homage of all peoples.

I have found through my own experiences and observations that the nurse, individually and collectively, usually manifests a kindness and good will that are representative of the finest characteristics of human nature.

It was during my month-long hospitalization in Chicago as a youth that I first became aware of these humanitarian traits. I was alone and scared, I had no money, and I could speak little English. The nurses went out of their way to make me feel at ease, were gentle and considerate.

I also saw them in action when I was in Europe,

after the First World War. Working under adverse conditions, they proved equal to any situation, quietly going about their business of dispensing mercy and alleviating suffering, often far beyond the normal requirements of their routine assignment. Their patients in that war theater were a motley lot, including every race, color, and creed, but I did not see then, nor have I seen since, any suggestion of racial or religious prejudice among nurses on duty.

My admiration for the nursing profession has held steadfast during the twenty-nine years of my work for the City of Hope. Many nurses have come and gone during those years—truly noble souls who never became hardened to human suffering and whose own interests were always sublimated to the needs of the patients.

While it may be true that the nurse is trained to alleviate suffering and to play an important role in healing, I believe her reaction to the cry of anguish and appeal for help goes far deeper than her allegiance to the Florence Nightingale oath. I believe there is good reason, too, for the fact that the huge majority of nurses are women. Since the female is the procreator and defender of life, hers is an innate response to any call from the helpless.

Yes, many nurses have earned my greatest respect for their interpretation and practice of "man's humanity to man." Their contribution to the creation and furtherance of the humanitarian principles embodied in the City of Hope program has been invaluable. Their sense of mercy is evidence, I believe, that they belong in the vanguard of man's march toward a better human society.

25

Doctors

AT THE TIME of Christ the span of human life is believed to have averaged about twenty-five years. Nineteen centuries later, it had reached forty-eight years, an increase of only twenty-three years in all those centuries.

The giant strides made by the medical profession in the past half-century are evidenced by the fact that twenty-one more years were added to the life expectancy of man in that comparatively short time.

Barring premature death as a result of war, accident, or disease, a human being alive today can anticipate a life's span of sixty-nine years. If the same rate of progress is maintained, there is no telling what the life expectancy may be of children born today. It can be assumed, however, that it will soon exceed that sixty-nine-year figure by a considerable margin.

The City of Hope is continually fighting disease,

the major cause of premature death, to help man round out the full span of his years on this earth —individually in its hospitals and clinics, and collectively through research, specialized medical education, and public information.

Since the saving and prolongation of human life is the nucleus around which our entire program is built, it is only natural that my work throughout the years brought me into closer contact with the medical profession than almost any other segment of our society. I therefore had an unusual opportunity, for a layman, to observe the problems of medical men, their nature as a group, and their relationships with one another and with their patients. I have also witnessed the gradual transition of the doctor from humanitarian, to technician, to businessman.

As a youth in Czarist Russia, my respect for the medical profession bordered on awe. Its members impressed me as superior beings who were entitled to an elevated position in society. In those days, doctors were scarce even in the big Russian cities, and in the rural district where I grew up they were practically unknown.

If statistics were available to show how many men, women, and children were born, lived, and died in Russia, without ever having a doctor at their bedsides, I believe the numbers would be astronomical. When a doctor did appear on the scene, he was a curiosity. His superior learning was evidenced by the use of medical terms no one could understand and he was revered by the humble people, admittedly his intellectual inferiors, for his ability to relieve pain and suffering and, above all, for his humanitarianism.

Because they were so scarce in rural areas, it is difficult for me personally to appraise the competence of doctors in those remote days. An incident of my own experience, however, leads me to believe that medical interference in the fight against disease at that time was more psychological than physical.

When I was twelve years old, I was stricken with a severe case of the mumps. As sometimes happens in the male, the disease caused a glandular swelling in the pelvic region—the existence of which was not freely acknowledged then. When the pain grew severe and my temperature continued to rise, my father departed for the nearest big city in search of a doctor, and after much effort succeeded in bringing one back with him.

Huge in stature, the doctor bore himself with a dignity that commanded respect and he was further distinguished by a full, perfectly groomed beard. Following his routine examination, he hinted that a member of the opposite sex must have been involved in his diagnosis and pressed me for a confession in order to corroborate his conclusion. I can still remember the frightening thoughts that coursed through my mind when I saw the glances of utter astonishment exchanged by my parents. At that point, I was scared enough to admit almost anything, but I was at a complete loss. I wanted to cooperate with the doctor but could not even create a mental image of the female in question, let alone produce a name for her.

It was not until some years later that I realized I had not been guilty as charged, and the doctor's erroneous diagnosis did not affect my reverence for his profession. I still considered its members as a class of society far above the ordinary run of man.

For many years after my arrival in the United States my experience with members of the medical profession was limited, more or less, to personal and family problems, except for my contacts with doctors in the army, during the First World War, and on my European mission following that war.

When I reached the sanatorium, however, the activities of the medical staff became closely interwoven with the pattern of my life at the institution and doctors became my daily companions. Throughout the years, many of them distinguished themselves in the service of the City of Hope, guiding its medical destinies from the day two tents were set up on a desert waste forty-one years ago until today, when the scope of our service is nationwide.

All of our doctors were instrumental in adding

"years to life," but in our efforts to establish a sound base for furthering our ideological program, I began to find many of them wanting on the spiritual front as it related to the adding of "life to years"—life with dignity!

I often had reason to wonder whether our medical schools had grown lax in preparing prospective doctors for the wide range of human relationships encompassed in their contacts with patients and the lay public in general. It may have been because of my close association with the doctors of the City of Hope that I had not become aware of the trend earlier. But as the years passed and we began to enlarge our medical staff, the deterioration in the doctor-patient relationship became more evident and, in my mind, began to constitute a threat to our belief that "there is no profit in curing the body if, in the process, we destroy the soul."

I was not able to account for this marked change in the makeup of our doctors and began to look further into the evolution of the medicine man to see if I could find some basis for it. My studies revealed a number of pertinent and interesting facts about the relationship of the ancients with their healers—facts which I believe have a direct bearing on our current problems.

When man first began to attach importance to the span of his life on this planet, he was troubled by two puzzling phenomena. A time came when the "spirit" left his physical body, and he then ceased to exist. As his mind developed through the ages, he found it increasingly difficult to make a mental adjustment to his mortality and never stopped searching for a more permanent dwelling place for his spirit than was afforded by his physical body.

When his search proved fruitless, he developed a compelling desire to keep the earthly abode of his spirit alive and in good repair as long as possible. He placed that heavy responsibility in the hands of a specially designated group variously known through the ages as medicine men, healers, physicians, and doctors.

The function of the medicine man was considered so important that he was given special inducements to assume the exacting role, and enjoyed singular economic privileges which left him free to devote undivided attention to the business of prolonging human life. In return for those unusual considerations, he was bound by oath to the fulfillment of his commission and was under threat of severe punishment for any lapses in the performance of his duty.

Having no scientific medical knowledge at that time, cures were accomplished through spiritual rather than technical intervention, and took on the aspect of "miracles" if and when the body was ultimately successful in fighting off the disease. It was the duty of the medicine man to invoke the assistance of any spiritual forces to which man gave credence at the various stages of his development. The spellbinding ceremonies used for that purpose were the forerunners of the quackery and faith healing rites which exist even in the face of today's scientific knowledge.

To offset the obvious lack of effective medical interference in the fight against disease, an ethical healer assumed the role of a "bedside" humanitarian. The unscrupulous practitioner, on the other hand, flourished during that era, able to practice his quackery because of man's unwillingness to accept mortality and his eagerness to try anything in the hope of delaying the inevitable.

At the turn of the twentieth century scientific medicine came into being and ushered in a new medical era. The wider horizons required a drastic change in medical education which, even in the finest schools up to that time, had consisted of only four months of lectures in each of two years, followed by an apprenticeship of sixteen months. (As recently as 1905, a high school education was not a prerequisite for admission to most medical schools.)

It was not until 1910 that sweeping reforms were instituted, largely through the efforts of Dr. Abraham Flexner, whose report on medical education in the United States and Canada aroused the profession to the need for a general housecleaning. A four-year course of training was introduced at that time but it was not until some years later that the four-year medical school curriculum became standard and hospital internship became an essential part of medical education.

There is no question that medical science has made great strides in the past half-century—gains in technical skill which gave impetus to the functional program of the City of Hope. We were excited by the evidence that medical interference was helping us prolong and save lives, but when it seemed that the doctor's technical proficiency had been gained at the expense of his humanitarianism we began to wonder whether we had not lost something indispensable in the transition. It was true that the new scientific developments helped to make hope more real but it was of equal importance that reality be made more hopeful. That is the fundamental basis for any satisfactory doctor-patient relationship.

But the doctor had become so preoccupied with his new technical skills, which in turn led to specialization, that he lost the personal touch. Why had he not been able to combine the two?

In the scramble for material things, our society had failed to take notice of the problems, unique to the medical profession, and had allowed the doctor to become just another businessman. He was permitted to descend from the high pedestal upon which he had been placed by the ancients and as he began to hobnob with the well-to-do, he found it necessary to enhance his economic status.

The more money the doctor had to have to keep up with the Joneses, the more patients he had to see and the more he had to charge; the more material possessions he accumulated, the more he had to protect his interests; the more time he spent on societies, lobbies, and political organizations, the less time he had to keep abreast with new medical developments; the less time he found to give each patient, the less satisfactory the doctor-patient relationship became and the more reason people had to turn to charlatans and faith healers.

That the lay public is responsible for this state of affairs is evident. That it will not tolerate the changed status of the doctor on a permanent basis is certain. After all, modern man has had no greater success in finding a permanent abode for his spirit than did his ancestors. Yet it is even more important to him that his body be kept alive and well. His more rational mind cannot as easily accept the various superstitions which satisfied his more credulous ancestors as likely abodes for the departed spirit.

It is no compliment to infinite mind, incidentally, that man's spirit is lodged in an abode of common clay. But as long as its dwelling place is governed by physical laws which exclude renewal of the lease, the "repair man" must be dedicated to the task of keeping the house in good condition as long as possible.

As long as man remains both physical and spiritual, the doctor must minister on both fronts and the significance of his role in our society rests upon the doctor-patient relationship. If technical skills have been achieved at the expense of that relationship, they have been bought too dearly.

Ignoring the problem can only lead to collectivism in medicine, which will defeat the purpose altogether by completely destroying the doctor-patient relationship. Even more, it will inhibit progress in the scientific field by curbing initiative and shackling the human mind.

What can be done about it? The prolongation and saving of human life is a full-time job. I believe we would do well to follow the example of the ancients and restore the modern medicine man to his former special status, providing for him certain economic privileges so that he can maintain a standard of living compatible with his important function. That would make it possible, once more, for the doctor to give service on a basis of humanitarianism instead of using the size of an anticipated fee as the yardstick.

To be sure, it will be a major task because human nature is involved. But man has succeeded in overcoming many of his innate characteristics before

163

now, and I am confident that by making a conscious and cooperative effort, the doctor and the lay public can together succeed in returning the medical profession to its former high estate.

In order to re-establish the doctor-patient relationship we should try to check, at the source, the trend away from that indispensable rapport. The profession might try to find a counterpart of Dr. Abraham Flexner and institute more exhaustive screening procedures for prospective medical students to determine whether they are truly interested in medicine for medicine's sake or whether they view the profession merely as a business venture.

Such general reforms cannot be accomplished overnight, but in time the profession must rid itself of those elements which have penetrated its ranks in the past and who continue to enter the profession for reasons other than a desire to serve mankind. It will have to cleanse itself of the quacks who prey on human misery for personal gain, and set straight or clear away those individuals who are honestly misguided in their thinking and so practice procedures which are not based on scientific fact. When the warm and assuring contact of the doctor-patient relationship is restored, the faith healers will lose their attraction and eventually fade away.

All these things can be brought about by an aroused and expressed public opinion—another People's Movement in medicine. Only a healthy nation is a strong nation. What is good for the American people, therefore, is good for the nation, and what is good for our nation at this turning point in civilization will, I feel, be good for all the peoples of the world.

26

Legacy

AND NOW, Irma, I have come to the still untouched leaves of my life's calendar. Which one of those remaining pages will bear the final entry is not for man to know. But I am satisfied to have recorded at least many heavily circled entries from the preceding pages. They mark the highlights of more than a half-century of my life on this planet.

I believe it is significant that my resolve to record these experiences and observations for you was inspired by the incident which occurred on the day of your birth. It was Christmas, a day when millions of people the world over were proclaiming, as they had for many centuries on Christmas Day, "Peace on earth, good will toward man!" Yet nations all over the world were then at one another's throats and you were called "Jew baby" within a few hours after your birth. Had only lip service been given to the ideal of good will toward men during all those centuries? I wondered.

The unreasoned intolerance of the young man who, himself, had probably paid reverent homage to another "Jew baby" in church that same morning, added a sense of mission to my life's work. On that Christmas Day of 1937, I rededicated myself to the purpose of making good will toward men more real by magnifying the humanitarian values fostered and practiced at the City of Hope and by developing apostles to give these values a wide circulation.

In the course of my fight for a better human society, I learned a lot about the why's and wherefore's of human behavior. My work brought me in close contact with people in all walks of life, under many different circumstances. I therefore had uncommon opportunities, I believe, for appraising and evaluating human actions and reactions.

My observations led me to believe that moral and spiritual strength are the handmaids of adversity and that both the mind and the body function most effectively in the face of obstacles. Personal handicaps represent a challenge which, in turn, rouses the spirit to action and creates a propelling force for human progress.

In my own case, it was the determination to overcome the handicaps of my immigrant status that impelled me to learn the language as soon as possible and to seek an education. The fact that I was a member of a minority group also intensified my eagerness to excel in all activities. I wanted to prove to myself and others that I merited the status of a first class citizen on the basis of notable contributions to my adopted homeland.

When I reached the sanatorium and began to work there, circumstances overwhelmingly verified that opinion. Those amazing people had inaugurated an institution to meet a vital human need without knowing where they might find the wherewithal to keep it going. Yet they accepted the challenge and their pioneering spirit brought the institution through one crisis after another.

History also bears out the fact that human progress stems from affliction. The Judaic concept upon which Western civilization is built was formulated and given to the world by the humble and the persecuted. The Sermon on the Mount is dedicated to an avowal that things of the spirit have their roots in adversity.

Many nations and empires grew strong and reached great heights while still in the throes of development. But once they began to feel smug and secure in their might and grew rich and overconfident, they became easy prey for the lowly whose struggle for survival had kept them physically strong and mentally alert.

Legacy

These facts do not mean that a nation must cultivate a parasitic segment of society, with power to exploit and persecute the meek, in order to provide a source of stimulation for progress. Not at all. They mean only that we must remain humble and strive for equality under the law while stubbornly maintaining the competitive stimulus inherent in cultural pluralism. I believe that a single culture is detrimental to human progress and that a nation derives the balance and counterbalance necessary to alertness and strength from a heterogeneous population.

In my opinion, the nation I chose for my homeland—the land of your birth—is vigorously blazing a trail in that direction by holding to established principles which have stood the test of the tempestuous half-century just passed. It is a doctrine which no other nation on earth has created and practiced to so great a degree.

The United States has furthered equality without destroying the yearnings of its people for the preservation of their respective ethnic cultures and, in turn, has been enriched and strengthened as a result of the integration of these separate heritages into its national life.

Our nation has abolished, outlawed, and ridiculed the caste system which, for so many centuries, has caused human misery and humiliation in other lands. It has established and granted human rights and

169

freedoms to people whose ancestors knew only slavery and persecution, and has also overcome poverty for a larger percentage of its people than any other nation in history.

What is especially noteworthy is that all these momentous phenomena came to pass without resorting to totalitarian regimentation or brute force. They evolved in the natural course of events through the efforts of our citizens who were determined to break with tradition and embrace new and progressive trends. It is true that often it has needed revolutions in other lands, or the threat of a revolution in our own, to open the eyes of some diehards to the dawning of new tomorrows. But whatever the means, we have succeeded in forging ahead toward desirable ends. We must never forget that these blessings did not full upon us like manna from heaven. Every forward step was achieved only by vigorous, vigilant, valiant men and women who loved liberty and justice.

That priceless heritage has been safeguarded through the years by an admixture of ingredients so potent in our national "body" that it has been able, repeatedly, to digest and excrete demagogues, bigots, would-be dictators, and all other elements bent upon its destruction. It is true that the invasion of those microbes often cause our nation to run a high fever but that, in itself, constitutes a defense.

The same currents and crosscurrents which helped

make our nation strong also built up a know-how which enables us to show the way to others—the way to bread and freedom for all. That is the most powerful secret weapon we have yet developed for world leadership.

We, the people of the United States of America, whose ancestors fled from slavery and persecution, we, who outlawed caste among our own people, who believe in equality under the law, who value human life and the dignity of the individual, who frown on political imperialism, and are on our way toward the abandonment of economic imperialism, must refuse to keep company with those nations which look with tolerance on the privileged few riding astride the backs of the many. We, as democratic, liberty-loving Americans, must extend our hands to the plowman in other lands, saying:

> *Give me your plow and I shall show you how to till your soil so that it will yield more abundantly. I offer my help to you not for gain or glory. I do it because you are my brother.*

That is the same basic principle upon which the City of Hope provides free service for those who have fallen by the wayside.

In the meantime, as we make ready for the society of the future in which the already fading physical boundaries of the world will be entirely obliterated, we must redouble our efforts to improve and strengthen the foundation upon which our national life is built. We must stay on the alert for and resist those ideological diseases which threaten our wholesome "constitution." We must strive for the kind of human society in which individual liberty and personal dignity will be everyone's right—a society which allows the privilege of a constructive nonconformity that releases the mind and spirit for creative and progressive achievement.

In developing our humanitarian philosophy at the City of Hope, I came to realize more than ever before that every generation leaves a legacy for those who follow. Contrary to Shakespeare's sentiment that "the evil that men do lives after them, the good is oft interred with their bones," I have learned that it is the good that men do which remains as a lasting heritage to posterity. Whether each leaves a little or a lot, their collective contributions make up the sum total of civilization at any given point. Perfection is not yet man's lot however, and the measure of human progress is still relative. We can, of course, conceive of a far better civilization than we have been able to create as yet, but it takes time for man to consolidate and apply the constructive ideas he inherits from preceding generations.

We, the people of the City of Hope, lay no claims to having discovered a new formula for the perfect human society. We believe only that it is possible for each succeeding generation to reach a higher level of civilization than the one before, if, individually and collectively, they make a conscious effort to overcome the baser instincts left over from darker eras. We believe, further, that there is a latent power for good in all mankind that can be brought to the surface *without threats of hell or hopes of paradise.*

One of the three pillars upon which our City of Hope program is built is *Reward.* In addition to the benefits which accrue to man in terms of spiritual nourishment derived from the sense of participation in our humanitarian work, the values created and fostered at the City of Hope remain as an enduring legacy for posterity—values which give our own lives meaning and direction and which, when handed down to our children, enrich their lives as well.

This record of my part in the development of that way of life is my legacy to you, Irma. It is a heritage which I consider of far greater value than a material one which I do not possess in any significant degree. For in the final analysis dollars are transient, spiritual values enduring.

In terms of twentieth century materialism, a legacy of this kind would be found wanting by many because worship of the dollar has distorted comparative values. Since man himself instituted marriage, home, and family for the purpose of perpetuating his ego and his possessions, his desire to leave an inheritance for his offspring is only natural. But the yardstick he is now using to measure the margin for their security has become warped.

Man's first and natural objective has always been the attainment of bread and security for himself and his family during his productive years, saving enough to assure his independence in old age, with a dividend left over for his children and even his children's children. But he has not learned—or perhaps has forgotten—where to stop. When he reaches a goal of thousands of dollars, he strives for millions, then for hundreds of millions. Amassing dollars for posterity becomes his life's work. Unless he amasses human values concurrently and proportionately, however, and inculcates them into his children, his untold material wealth becomes a millstone around their necks. Not only are they deprived of the physical and spiritual fortitude which are the by-products of facing and overcoming constructive challenges, but they are denied the joy of achievement through their own efforts.

When I see the havoc wrought by some of the tremendous dollar legacies of recent years and the unhappiness they bring to generation after generation, I seem to hear the voice of my boyhood teacher echoing back through the years once again, as he declaims the words of the prophet Amos:

Woe unto them that are of ease in Zion and secure in
the mountains of Samaria; they who lie upon couches
of ivory and stretch themselves lazily upon their beds
and eat rams from the flock and feed on calves from
the stall; they who thrum the harp and drink chalices
of fine wine and anoint themselves with precious
oils. . . .

I often wonder at the vision of the sages who formulated those adages which are as applicable today
as they were many centuries ago.

In recording these experiences and observations
for you, I have held almost entirely to the short-
range point of view. For after all, man is nearest to
himself and more concerned with matters pertaining to relationships with his fellow man and the welfare of his immediate posterity than he is with the
ultimate destiny of the human race.

But in shaping our lives, there is a long-range point
of view which we must bear in mind, even though
it is in the realm of speculation. The human race
is a comparatively new species on this earth and has
no precedent by which to judge its ultimate destiny
with any degree of certainty.

We know that many other species of animal life,
which existed on this planet for millions of years,
finally became extinct for one reason or another, and
who knows but that extinction may not be man's lot
as well.

We may reason, logically, that those other forms of animal life did not have the intuition with which to build up defenses against current dangers and that man, who has developed the most potent of all defense mechanisms—a mind—will therefore escape their fate.

That may well be, but there is another consideration. The physical body has not kept pace with the development of its spiritual tenant. It is within the realm of probability, therefore, that the human mind may itself become the Frankenstein monster which will be the very instrument of its own destruction.

Despite any evidence to the contrary, though, we must carry on in the confidence that human destiny is spiritual perfection, and live our lives accordingly. Defeatism can only militate against human progress by discouraging mankind from exerting every effort to overcome the obstacles which bar his way to the achievement of a perfect and permanent human society.

Realistically, while all of us may be born equal under the law, we are not all born at the same stage of intellectual development. I believe that a large segment of the human race is already scaling the wall of the next cycle in our civilization and that those in that category must be given the freedom to advance to higher rungs on the ladder in order to make way for those who wish to follow. That vanguard is the hope of us who mount confidently on the lower rungs, and it is up to us to see that their progress is not hampered by the chains of outmoded tradition.

We, the people of the City of Hope, have accepted the challenge of building a better world for ourselves and our posterity because we believe that this should be man's mission on earth. It is our sincere hope that the human values created and tested in the spiritual laboratories of the City of Hope will be an effective antidote for the materialism rampant in our twentieth century society. If our hope is realized, our reward will be the knowledge that we have left an enduring legacy to posterity.

In the words of Rabbi Saul of Tarsus:

> I beseech ye, therefore, to have your turn of mind free from the love of money. For the love of money is a root of all kinds of evil from which some reaching after have been led astray from the faith and have pierced themselves through with many sorrows. Let them do good, being rich in good works, that they may be ready to store for themselves a good treasure against the time to come, that they may lay hold on the life which is life indeed.